CARIBBEAN LITERATURE:
AN ANTHOLOGY

Caribbean Literature

AN ANTHOLOGY
selected and edited by

G. R. COULTHARD   B.A., Ph.D.

 UNIVERSITY OF LONDON PRESS LTD

UNIVERSITY OF LONDON PRESS LIMITED
ST PAUL'S HOUSE WARWICK LANE LONDON EC4

Copyright © 1966 G. R. Coulthard

Printed in Great Britain by Richard Clay (The Chaucer Press) Limited
Bungay Suffolk

CONTENTS

INTRODUCTION

Writing about the Caribbean area could be said to begin with Columbus's letters to the King of Spain, in which he describes the lands and the peoples he discovered. Indeed, many histories of Latin American literature start with a chapter on the writing *about* the New World. In the case of the Caribbean, the most widely read accounts of the early days of the conquest and settlement are Gonzalo Fernández de Oviedo's *General History of the Indies* (1539) and Father Bartolomé dé Las Casas's *A Short Account of the Destruction of the Indies* (1552), in which the good father writes a passionate denunciation of the cruelty of the Spanish conquistadors and colonists. This work, which is full of vivid detail and description, can certainly be regarded as a work of literature, and in fact many modern apologists of the Spanish empire in America claim that it is largely a work of the imagination rather than a historical document.

In the French West Indies a key work is Father J. B. Labat's account of the history and customs of the Indies. This work, published in 1722, is full of acute observations, picturesque local colour and humorous anecdote.

From the British Caribbean vivid and picturesque descriptions of life in the islands are provided by the novelist Matthew (Monk) Lewis in his *Journal of a West Indian Proprietor 1815–17*, the *Diary of Lady Nugent* (1839) and Anthony Trollope's *West Indies and the Spanish Main* (1859).

It should be borne in mind that these works were written by foreigners viewing the Caribbean from a European point of view. Some are more in the form of histories and chronicles, but they are the only means by which we can get a picture of what life was like in the Caribbean in the past. They have also served as source material for many Caribbean novelists and poets. Good examples of this are Jesús de María Galván's novel about the Indian chieftain Enriquillo who led a spirited resistance against the Spaniards in Santo Domingo, translated into English by Robert Graves as *The*

Cross and the Sword. There is also *Anacaona*, by the Dominican poetess Salomé Ureña de Henríquez. This work deals with the tragic death of the Indian Queen Anacaona, whom the Spaniards led into an ambush and subsequently hanged. The historical matter for both these works is largely Las Casas and Juan de Castellanos's *Elegies for Great Men of the Indies.*

It is in the Spanish islands of Cuba and Santo Domingo that we find the first signs of a national literature, that is, of a literature reflecting the feelings of native writers. Although Cuba remained a Spanish colony until 1898, it produced in the person of José Maria de Heredia a poet whose works are known throughout the Spanish-speaking world. Heredia, who felt and wrote as a Cuban, spent most of his life in exile in Mexico for conspiring against Spanish colonial rule. Cuba also produced a number of anti-slavery novels such as Anselmo Suárez Romero's *Francisco* written in 1839, and Cirilo Villaverde's *Cecilia Valdés* started also in 1839 but not finally published until 1882 in New York. Both these novels give, as well as a picture of the horrors of slavery, designed to inspire disgust, a lively and colourful account of the atmosphere of Cuba in the early nineteenth century. *Cecilia Valdés* in particular is regarded as one of the classics of Cuban literature.

Although a great deal of literature was produced in Cuba, Santo Domingo, Haiti and the French West Indies in the nineteenth century, very little of it is of a high literary quality. The subjects are Caribbean, indeed very deliberately so, but much of the writing is amateurish. The great Nicaraguan poet Ruben Darío writing at the end of the last century said, "Most of our writers are completely ignorant of the art they are trying to practise." This generalization, meant for Latin America, is certainly true of the Caribbean.

While literature of a sort was being produced in the Spanish and French Caribbean in the nineteenth century, the British West Indies were culturally asleep. When a literature did begin to emerge in the early years of this century, it was provincial, imitative and slip-shod. J. E. Clare McFarlane, for example, in the 1920s was writing paraphrases of Wordsworth and Tennyson. Herbert Delisser wrote novels on Jamaican life, but most of them are hardly readable today, even his *White Witch of Rose Hall*, which is a good story. The reason is that Delisser did not know how to write a novel.

He had no concept of style, no idea of construction and the psychology of his characters is superficially and insensitively handled.

In the Spanish and French Caribbean, however, there was a definite maturing after 1920. Writers began to regard themselves as professionals, and attempted—and in some cases succeeded—in measuring up to international standards. This was largely the result of a movement all over Latin America known as *modernism*, which affirmed that in order to create a national literature it was not enough just to write about national subjects. After the modernists' revulsion against Latin American subject-matter, writers returned to the same subjects, but with a new awareness that they must take stylistic considerations into account. Cuban writers such as Nicolás Guillén, Alejo Carpentier, the Martinican Aimé Césaire and the Puerto Rican, Luis Palés Matos, are internationally known and accepted.

There was definitely a connection in the British Caribbean between the awakening of a national consciousness and a desire for independence and the burgeoning of a new national literature, which set itself higher standards than those hitherto accepted. Writing in the first number of the magazine *Focus* in 1943, Mrs. Edna Manley said, "Great and irrevocable changes have swept this land in the last few years and out of these changes a new art is springing."

And this 'new art', this new impulse found its first outlet principally in the literary magazines *Focus*, published in Jamaica, and *Bim*, published in Barbados. Many writers who have subsequently become known throughout the English-speaking world, and indeed have been translated into French, Spanish, German, Portuguese and other languages, tried their wings in the pages of these magazines. Outstanding among them are the Jamaicans Vic Reid and John Hearne; the Trinidadian Samuel Selvon and the Guianese Edgar Mittelholzer.

Perhaps the most remarkable feature of British Caribbean writing since the later 1940s is its high literary quality, or at least the high literary standards which writers set themselves. Such writers as V. S. Naipaul, John Hearne and Derek Walcott measure themselves against the best in world writing.

9

Now for the purpose of this anthology 'Caribbean' is being used to mean the islands of the Caribbean Sea, and one of the first questions that must arise is: Is there such a thing as a Caribbean literature as opposed to a literature produced in the Caribbean area? Opinions certainly vary on this point, and indeed the style and handling of material varies widely even within a given island. Writers born in the Caribbean and using the Caribbean scene in their works often protest that they are not Caribbean or West Indian writers but merely writers who happen to have been born in a particular geographical area. Some even object to being called Cuban or Jamaican writers and state that they are poets, novelists or playwrights, and that their place of origin is of no significance. What they seem to be objecting to is the imposition of a set of local themes and the assumption that for geographical reasons they are possessed of a common or similar kind of temperament and literary sensibility.

Other writers in the Caribbean, on the other hand, affirm loudly that they have a distinctive personality, and some go so far as to claim that it is the duty of the writer, at least for the present, to set himself the task of interpreting his environment through his specially conditioned way of experiencing life, which is peculiarly Caribbean.

It might not be irrelevant at this point to state that this same problem has arisen in the Latin American countries where cultural nationalism has been strong since the early nineteenth century. Many writers, however, have rejected cultural nationalism, claiming that they are Mexicans, Colombians, Chileans, etc., who write novels, plays or poems, and are in no way bound to reflect the national or even the Latin American scene.

Whatever concept writers may hold of themselves, the critic who takes a broad view of writing in the Caribbean cannot escape the conclusion that there is an air of similarity about much of it. This is obviously due, to some extent, to the similarity of the historical background and human environment, to the flora and fauna, to the very landscape and climatic conditions. The historical background in all the islands has followed the same pattern: discovery and conquest by the Spaniards; extermination of the native Indian populations and their replacement by slave-labour from Africa; the introduction of sugar and the world of the sugar estate, both during and after slavery; and independence at varying dates (Haiti first in 1804, with Jamaica and Trinidad gaining their independence as late as 1962). All the islands have known the common experience of colonialism, exploitation, poverty and economic frustration. In all the islands racial discrimination has been a problem, and racial resentments and complexes continue to be an important factor. The last twenty-five years have seen the growth of a middle class in all the islands, living largely on borrowed values (either American, British or French), and an intelligentsia seeking urgently a spiritual and cultural orientation of its own.

It should perhaps be pointed out that there are some major differences, notably between the violent, blood-stained history of Cuba, the Dominican Republic and Haiti, and the comparatively tranquil development of the ex-British and French colonies. The ex-British and French colonies have not experienced the horrors of military dictatorship and civil wars which the Spanish-speaking islands have suffered. The vast range of material that such events supply to the writer is totally alien to them.

It is obvious that the conditions referred to offer abundant subject-matter to the poet, novelist or playwright, and indeed they have been widely drawn on.

What techniques the writer applies in the handling of this material will depend on his own ability, literary experience and personal choice.

Another factor which has been adduced to account for the particular flavour of Caribbean writing, indeed of Caribbean music, painting and dancing, is the presence of the Negro. As the Puerto Rican poet, Luis Palés Matos puts it: "The Negro lives physically and spiritually within us all, and his characteristics, filtered down through the mulatto, influence in a very apparent way every mani-festation of the life of our people." Other writers, particularly in the French West Indies and in Haiti, have proclaimed that the whole cultural outlook of the coloured West Indian should be, and prob-ably basically is, African rather than European. The Haitian novelist, Jacques Stéphen Alexis, stated recently in a conference of Negro writers and artists in Paris that all people who have their origin in Africa display a notable permanence of cultural features and that works of art produced by people in countries of African origin are more readily 'felt' by men of Negro origin than any other kinds of art. "Our art [i.e. Haitian art and the art of all peoples of Negro origin] tends to the exact sensuous representation of reality, to creative intuition, to character and expressive power."

Whether or not there exists a common Caribbean sensibility is an open question, and the reader of this anthology may draw his own conclusions. The criterion of selection is based on what is most typical in the work of Caribbean writers of established literary reputation.

George Campbell

Most of George Campbell's poems were originally published in the Jamaican magazine *Focus*, 1943 and 1948 editions. He belonged in fact to the 'Focus group', which was closely associated with the Jamaican independence movement in the 1940s. His subjects are the common people of Jamaica, particularly the peasants, the Negro in Jamaica and elsewhere, and the distress and hopelessness of the poor. His social idealism and proclamations of the beauty and dignity of the Negro are expressed in an exalted, emphatic idiom, at times with strong Biblical overtones.

George Campbell was one of the first Jamaican poets to break away from the strangle-hold of Victorianism, which had characterized Jamaican poetry in the first three decades of the twentieth century, and when his poems first appeared in Jamaica they appealed on account of their directness and freedom from conventional rhetoric.

HOLY BE THE WHITE HEAD OF A NEGRO

Holy be the white head of a Negro.
Sacred be the black flax of a black child.
Holy be
The golden down
That will stream in the waves of the winds
And will thin like dispersing clouds.
Holy be
Heads of Chinese hair
Sea calm sea impersonal
Deep flowering of the mellow and the traditional.
Heads of peoples fair.
Bright shimmering from the riches of their species;
Head of Indians
With feeling of distance and space and dusk;
Heads of wheaten gold
Heads of people dark
So strong so original:
All of the earth and sun.

Oh Solomon's fair
Oh shadowed flower.

Not black
blue sky in face.

Oh woven of the night
this beauty of her race.

Oh glorious peak
procreative power
the woman Eve
twixt dark and light
Oh Solomon's fair
Oh shadowed flower.

Errol Hill

Errol Hill, born in Trinidad in 1921, has pioneered the growth of a West Indian theatre and play-form by writing plays, acting, producing and teaching drama. Most of his plays have been performed in various parts of the West Indies, and a number have been published, mainly by the Extra-Mural Department of the University of the West Indies. His best known works are *The Ping-pong*, a play of the Trinidad steel band, *Strictly Matrimony*, a satire on Jamaican mass-marriages, and *Man Better Man*, a folk play with music and dance chosen as the entry from Trinidad and Tobago at the 1965 Commonwealth Arts Festival in Britain.

In his work Errol Hill tends to satire and comedy, and makes full and at times poetic use of the popular speech of Trinidad. As a producer and drama tutor, he has a strong sense of the stage and his plays are very actable.

DANCE BONGO—*a fantasy in one act**

PERSONS IN THE PLAY

A Stranger	*Preacher*
Orange Vendor	*Jeremy*
Old Woman	*Gaby*
1st Woman	*Tom*
2nd Woman	*Chantrelle*
1st Man	*Villagers*
2nd Man	

A clearing in a village settlement; late afternoon

AUTHOR'S NOTE: The Bongo is a native dance of Trinidad and Tobago derived from Africa. It is danced at wakes for the dead and was originally symbolic of regeneration. Nowadays it is performed mainly for entertainment.

The Preacher is a leader of one of the native religious cults practised in the country.

* Performance of this play may be given only with the author's permission, in writing, and on payment of a royalty fee. All enquiries should be addressed to: Mr. Errol Hill, University of the West Indies, St. Augustine, Trinidad, W.I.

A clearing in a village settlement in the low hills. Near by a hut topped by a cross serves as a church. Shade trees. An orange vendor. Two women shelling peas, one smoking a clay pipe. An old woman swaying and humming a dirge. Two men playing checkers.

Late afternoon. Silence and stillness but for the dirge, the nimble fingers shelling, the tap-tap on the checkers-board.

Stranger enters.

Stranger	Any body dead bout here, today?
	Any body dead or dying?
Vendor	No body dead since Samuel pass
	And leave the world a-sighing.
1st Woman	Ay, what a day when news appear
	Galloping like revelation,
	The crane collapse and kill a man——
2nd Woman	It shake my soul foundation
	Missis, to think that morning self
	I put his butter-bread one side
	Knowing he would o' smiling come
	To fetch it evening-time.
	And poor little Susan, how she cry
	When they drop him in the hole,
	He had promise to bring her back a toy.
1st Woman	So sudden! The world turn upside-down
	When the young go and the old remain.
	The hand of God in everything
	And we must bow before his will.
	(*Old Woman moans louder.*)
Vendor	Hush, Teena, hush, old Sarah still
	Considering the boy
	Who was the prop against her age,
	The promise of her joy
	Now gone for good.
2nd Woman	The Lord be praised!
	It happen pon a while
	When everybody did well prepare
	To send him off in style.
	Josey did just brew up some whites,

16

	I did bake, and Tom
	Had tobacco-leaf drying in his yard—
1st Woman	Gaby did buy a drum
	And wanted cause to christen it——
2nd Woman	True, we send him as a king
	All right with the whole village rejoicing.
	Only he leave one old woman behind
	Crying, always crying.
Vendor	Miss Sarah, you want anything?
	(Old Woman stops moaning and stares into space.)
Stranger	How long he dead? What time gone by?
	You keep the nine-night yet?
1st Woman	Long time, my son, five months today.
Old Woman	The old never forget.
	The young heal quick when they have hurt,
	Like scratches on the shore
	They soon erase, but the old brain
	Is scarred for ever more.
1st Woman	Sarah soul, don't fret-up yourself
	Again, is best you keep
	The little strength you have to live
	In peace, don't wail and weep.
Old Woman	Alas! that in this twilight time
	Of life my tired soul
	Should know no rest until that crime
	Is paid a hundred-fold.
2nd Woman	No crime at all, the magistrate
	Rule, was an accident,
	The crane collapse, who here would want
	Sammy to meet that fate?
	Not me, not Teena, Tom or Liz.
	Not Josey, call any name
	Not Jeremy his buddy sure
	Though he was chief to blame.
	Anyhow Sam gone and all your cries
	Can't bring him back again.
Vendor	Leave her, Maisie, who to know

	How sorrow stun the heart
	Torn open by a sudden blow,
	Leave her to mourn her pain.
	(*To Stranger*)
	Who are you looking for? What it is you want?
Stranger	This village name Cedarpost?
2nd Woman	That self. Who it is you come to find
	Creeping up like a ghost.
	You is police? Nobody here
	Ain't do nothing wrong, I say.
Stranger	Lady, I looking for a dead
	Or dying man today.
1st Woman	Is your family? I sorry bad.
	Mother or father side?
	Josey, the mister looking for
	A relative what died.

(*The Men look up from checkers-board, stare at Stranger curiously, then resume their game.*)

2nd Woman	What's your title? Since I living here
	Only six people gone——
	No seven—counting Miss Fraser child
	What dead before it born.
	Papa John went in thirty-two,
	He was man-and-a-half,
	Old as he was he still could burst
	Your side in two with laugh.
	And rude! the man ain't——
Vendor	Maisie, I beg you
	Let the mister finish speak
	What name you say you looking for?
Stranger	I don't rightly know who I seek.
	Any body sick, here or hereabout,
	Any body have ache or pain
	Enough to want a quick relief? Who heart
	Does stumble under the strain
	Of living? Madam, you feeling all right
	Now? You ain't hurting nowhere?
	Mister, what bout you, you keeping well——

1st Man	Haul your dry tail out o' here.
	You interrupting people game.
Stranger	Ask pardon——
2nd Man	Go-way!
Stranger	No body at all sick bad in the village?
	Then I get led astray.
	Since sun wake-up I travelling
	To reach here before night,
	And now you tell me is some mistake.
	(*He looks around trying to identify the village.*)
	Kind people, give me a bite
	Of food, I hungry.
Vendor	It have orange in the tray,
	Five cents apiece. How much
	You want? Peel already, they two-
	For-nine. Eh, eh, don't touch
	Them up if you please.
	(*Stranger has moved to the tray; now he turns desperately.*)
Stranger	I never meet
	Such a well village in all my life!
	(*shouting*)
	Any body sick in the settlement here!
	Any body tired of stress and strife!
	Any body soul tugging to get free
	And join the spirits of land and sea
	Swirling away in an ecstasy!
	Speak now, and let me dance for thee!
Old Woman	(*shrieks in pain*)
	Ayee, ayee. I feel him near,
	His hand upon my heart
	To stop it beating. Sammy son,
	Precious boy, you want me there?
	Not yet, not yet, a criminal
	Does lord it on the ground
	Where you was king over all and all
	Your old friends now acknowledge him.
	But I will live and plot and plan

To topple him from the throne,
To make him eat the dirt like you
In a dark hole alone,
No peace until your bosom friend
Snake-in-the-grass Jeremy
Come face to face with a violent end
Then I will come to you.
Ayee, ayee . . .

(*Her voice rises in a spasm of grief. The Women run
to comfort her. Vendor pours some rum into a glass
and gives it to Old Woman. Dusk. The men put up
their checkers-board. Vendor lights a flambeau on her
tray. The Women take up their shelling utensils and
lead Old Woman off. Stranger sits on stool previously
occupied by Old Woman. The Men cross and stand
over Stranger.*)

1st Man	So you is a dancer? What kind o' dancer?
Stranger	I dance the bongo.
2nd Man	You dance the bongo?
Stranger	I dance the bongo.
1st Man	Why you frighten the old woman?
Stranger	She frighten herself.

She feel the pain of parting with life
And she frighten herself,
She frighten herself.

2nd Man	What you come here for?
Stranger	I will tell you in fine.

I go where I'm needed, I get there in time,
It is my profession to know where to go,
I read the papers, I hear radio,
I see it in dreams, awake or asleep,
I feel where I'm needed
To dance the bongo,
I follow my pulse, wherever it lead
Me, I follow prepared
To dance the bongo
As I dance for the dead.

1st Man   Your pulse lead you to Cedarpost Village?

Stranger	Yes.
1st Man	It lead you astray. Hello and goodbye.
	No body don't want your service tonight.
	Beside if you living you surely must know
	No place on earth can dance the bongo
	Like Cedarpost Village. So Stranger, ill met,
	Keep moving, this ain't your harbour of death
	(*Stranger remains seated.*)
2nd Man	You didn't hear what the man say?
	Keep moving, boy,
	Like you want me throw you out.
Stranger	(*to himself*)
	It will solve nothing, what is to be
	Will be regardless of violent men.
	Solve nothing but spawn
	More violence and pain,
	Yet when in the cedar the violent worm
	Brings a high head to rest on the belly of earth,
	Earth open her door to rescue her own,
	Worm, wood and body together at last.
	(*to the Men*)
	Cedarpost is a pretty village,
	You wouldn't spoil it?
1st Man	You ain't leaving?
Stranger	Soon—but not yet.
1st Man	(*to 2nd Man*)
	I going call the Preacher.
	Watch him like a snake.
	(*He goes into the church.*)
Stranger	(*to Vendor*)
	Lady, I beg you an orange please!
Vendor	Five cents apiece, two-for-nine peel.
2nd Man	Bring one, but let him peel it heself.
	(*Vendor brings orange and knife. Stranger takes orange, but looks at knife in horror and declines to touch it. He strips orange peel with his fingers and eats during the scene that follows.*)
2nd Man	This village have fame all over the land

	For the bongo we dance.
	They come from city and suburb and town
	To see us perform.
	We go to the city, we travel around,
	We dance independence, we dance carnival,
	We dance in the night-clubs wherever we can,
	Cedarpost Bongo is known in the land.
Stranger	I dance for the dead.
2nd Man	We dance for the children with chattering eyes,
	We dance for the ladies who cross their thighs,
	We dance for princes, politicians and priests,
	For all who would tame the marauding beasts
	That feast on the soul, we dance and we sing.
	Cedarpost Bongo is known in the land.
Stranger	I dance for the dead.
2nd Man	We win all the prizes, we have the best dancers,
	We dance in the village for weddings and parties,
	We dance upon birthdays, Saturdays, holidays,
	We dance upon paydays, or even on Sundays,
	We dance when a bottle is broken or open,
	We dance till the earth itself moans with emotion.
	Cedarpost Bongo is known in the land.
Stranger	I dance for the dead.
2nd Man	You is a good dancer?
Stranger	The best in the land!
2nd Man	Jeremy Jordan is best in the land,
	And Samuel Seaton before him was best,
	And Hanif Mohammed before him was best,
	And Manuel Temoya before him was best,
	Before and before, they all come from here,
	For Cedarpost Bongo is best in the land.
	You is a good dancer?
Stranger	The best in the world!
2nd Man	Jeremy Jordan is best in the world!
	Son of Josiah, the best in the world!
	Before him was Samuel, old Sarah grandson——
Stranger	I dance for the dead.
	(*Enter 1st Man and Preacher. They cross to Stranger.*

The Man carries a lantern. Preacher is dressed in long white robes, sandals, and wears a long beard, but he is not an old man. Hatless. His manner is grave, almost sad. Vendor crosses to join group.)

1st Man	*(to Stranger)*
	Stand up for the Preacher.
	(He stands.)
Preacher	Where you come from, boy?
Stranger	Lopinot, Tabaquite, Barrackpore, all,
	Wherever, whatever place-name you call
	I been there, or going or coming from there.
Preacher	You is a traveller?
Stranger	Yes.
Preacher	A dancer? A bongo dancer?
Stranger	Yes.
Preacher	A good bongo dancer?
Stranger	Best between earth and sky.
Preacher	You hear that, Josiah?
1st Man	Yes, Preacher, I hear.
Preacher	You dance for money?
Stranger	No, Preacher-man.
Preacher	Then you come to compete
	Gainst the men in the village?
Stranger	Not so, Preacher-man.
Preacher	Bongo and Cedarpost marry together
	Long time in history, boy.
	What the almighty see fit to endeavour
	Don't seek to destroy.
	If you hungry we'll feed you,
	Reclothe and refresh you,
	Even give money to purchase godspeed,
	Our church is a charity for all who in need,
	Only leave us the peace,
	And leave us tonight.
Stranger	Kind is your cloth, Preacher-man,
	I accept your sweet hospitality
	Being in need. And in turn promise
	To take leave tomorrow

23

	Or maybe tonight
	But after the dance.
Preacher	What dance, boy?
Stranger	After the bongo, Preacher-man.
Preacher	It have bongo tonight, Josiah?
1st Man	No, Preacher, no.
Preacher	Obadiah?
2nd Man	No, Preacher.
Preacher	As you see, boy, no bongo tonight.
	Come into the church for a rest and a prayer,
	Later you'll leave refreshed and recovered——
Stranger	(*as they move off*)
	After the dance.
	(*Preacher and Stranger go into the church.*)
1st Man	Best bongo dancer! Lie! lie! lie!
Vendor	Jeremy Jordan is better than he.
1st Man	Best between earth and sky!
2nd Man	Best in the world, he say.
1st Man	Better than my Jeremy!
2nd Man	Best in the land, he say.
1st Man	Lie! lie! lie!
	Jeremy Jordan is best in the land.
Vendor	Cedarpost Bongo is best in the world.
1st Man	Call Jeremy, go look for him,
	Wherever he may be,
	Down by the wharf, up on the crane,
	Bring him back cagily.
2nd Man	It getting late, is far to go,
	Maybe I search in vain,
	Maybe the young man leave before
	I reach and come back again.
1st Man	Call Jeremy, he can't be far,
	Wherever he may be
	This threat will fester in his ear
	And fetch him home in a hurry.
Vendor	Cedarpost Bongo is better than he!
	(*She returns to sit beside her tray.*)
2nd Man	Jeremy bongo far and wide,

24

	Never a shade of dread, Wherever the drums and the kwa-kwa beat, Except when Sammy dead.
Vendor	Ay, that one time he couldn't creep Out of his corner of grief, His mortal limbs did crumple-up Into a sorrowing heap.
1st Man	But now he will dance like a demon king Deep in the heart of the wood, Rattle the bamboo and drums together To hustle home his blood.
Vendor	Best bongo dancer! (*She laughs derisively.*) He! he! he!
2nd Man	Jeremy Jordan is better than he.
All	Cedarpost Bongo is best in the land! (*Vendor puts on old jacket against the night air. A flashlight approaches. Jeremy and Gaby enter. Gaby carries a drum slung over his shoulder and a bottle of rum in his pocket.*)
Jeremy	I hear the echo of a drum Or a bottle sudden groan, Drink or drum it hustle my soul And lead it straightway home. So what all you doing? Fête tonight?
Gaby	We come prepare for emergency, On my back a brand-new drum And a full square in my back pocket.
Jeremy	So what is the racket?
1st Man	You too tired to dance?
Jeremy	Tired? Day and night I does dance Working the crane or carting the load, Whatever have power, zip or life Is a partner to dance with, Drink and desire with. The drum Have a life all its own, and the rum Invest with a spirit of devilry, Put them together and bongo make three,

25

	Three dwell together in one unity.
	What you have in mind?
1st Man	Bongo tonight.
Jeremy	So bongo tonight,
	Is nothing so rare.
2nd Man	A man come to bongo, come from far
	In the shade of the deepening sun,
	Soft as a shade he come,
	Come here to bongo, lithe as a leaf
	He float in the ground
	Where we do the bongo, saying,
	This stranger-man, he do the best bongo,
	The best in the land.
All	Cedarpost Bongo is best in the land!
2nd Man	Best in the world, he say.
All	Cedarpost Bongo is best in the world.
2nd Man	He in with the Preacher there,
	Inside the church.
Jeremy	Well, go fetch him out
	Maybe he can teach,
	Gaby start up a beat
	We go stand by and watch.
	But first, Lizzy gal, my throat kind o' parch,
	Cut two sweet orange, slit them high in the throat,
	And put salt in the wound, to give it a zip.
Gaby	(*producing the rum*)
	Any body want fire? The night making cold.
	Though the moon have a flambeau up
	Still the night making cold.
	(*The men drink straight from the bottle, saluting it as they drink. Vendor brings oranges to Jeremy. She returns to tray and takes a drink from her own bottle of rum.*)
1st Man	Fuel for the blood! (*Drinks.*)
2nd Man	Fuel for the dance! (*Drinks.*)
Gaby	Let the fuel burn bright
	In the heat of the dance! (*Drinks.*)
Vendor	And the fire will rise

	From earth to the skies
	Till the moon swell so big
	She will burst with surprise! (*Drinks.*)
	(*Laughter.*)
Jeremy	(*taking the bottle*)
	Now spirit of madness
	Possess me tonight,
	Enter and express
	The power I possess.
	Let nothing divide us
	Or crib or confine us,
	Nothing prohibit the fling of the dance.
	Tonight we will fly between earth and sky
	In holy bongo, in holy bongo! (*Drinks.*)
1st Man	Roll the drum, Gaby,
	Rally a chorus,
	The beaters and singers with bamboo and voices
	To back up the dancers with kwa-kwa and chorus,
	Reach them, pull them out, from every quarter,
	Living or loving, in sleep or carousing,
	Bring them together, child, mother and father,
	All who will answer
	The call to bongo.
	(*Gaby rolls the drums. Voices come in with rhythmic, repetitive chorus: "Cedarpost Bongo!" Men run in carrying lighted flambeaux or candles with bamboo slats for kwa-kwa beating. Flambeaux are placed on the ground in a semi-circle. Some hold candles, others beat bamboo, all move to rhythm and swell chorus until Jeremy holds up his hand for silence.*)
Drums	Ta-ti/ta/ti-ti/ta-ti-ta.
Voices	Cedarpost Bongo!
Jeremy	So where is the Stranger-man,
	This dangerous wonder-man,
	Who profess to know
	The secret of bongo?
	Where this professor of dance
	Who going teach

	Men born in a spasm of deliverance
	To dance?
2nd Man	He in with the Preacher
	There in the church.
	You want me to call him?
Voices	Yes, bring him out!
Jeremy	No. Let him be.
	If the music ain't call him,
	Ain't quicken and control him,
	He don't belong here,
	Let him sleep on a prayer.
Vendor	A sly man is he who slide in between
	The covers of evening to whisper a charge
	The cedar trees take to the village at large:
	He is the best dancer between earth and sky.
Voices	Lie! lie! lie!
	Cedarpost Bongo is best in the world!
1st Man	I going call him out.
Jeremy	No, I say no,
	Leave him let him pray.
	He know what a sacrifice
	Coming will bring.
	But beat bamboo and drum,
	Is bongo tonight,
	Forget the grave Stranger
	And pass round the rum.
	(*Again the drum, kwa-kwa and voices merge. Now a chantrelle leads the singing.*)
Chantrelle	Bongo dance was a mystery,
& Chorus	Cedarpost Bongo!
	Cedar man take and marry she,
	Cedarpost bongo!
	One by one the children come,
	Cedarpost bongo!
	Feed on kwa-kwa and the Congo drum,
	Cedarpost bongo!
	Now we master the bongo art,
	Cedarpost bongo!

	Feel it beating inside your heart!
	Cedarpost bongo!
	Dance the bongo until you dead,
	Cedarpost bongo!
	But dance it first on top the bed,
	Cedarpost bongo!
	(*Music heightens. Several men detach from chorus and begin to dance. Preacher and Stranger enter. Bongo stops.*)
Preacher	Josiah, you say no bongo tonight.
1st Man	So I say, Preacher, but Jeremy come.
Jeremy	And Gaby wanting to christen he drum.
Preacher	No bongo, you say, yet now you begin
	To fasten a knot that nobody know
	Whose neck it will fit. So we hope and pray,
	And all the time time is gnawing away
	At the peace. In the church
	We just finish pray for all the good who
	Release before, or after their time
	But always in time, and those still to go.
	And now you commence to dance the bongo.
Jeremy	But, Preacher, we always dance when we merry,
	And Gaby bring also a bottle of rum.
Preacher	What happen, happen always in time,
	So nothing ever repeat just the same.
	You dance yesterday, last night, and now,
	And soon you will start up again, but each
	Is a separate bongo starting, containing,
	Continuing the first-ever bongo that dance.
1st Man	I don't follow you, Preacher.
Preacher	Never mind. The dance will go on and on
	Whether we join in or hinder or stop
	The dance will go on. And when the drum cease
	The echo will come sounding through the peace
	To continue the dance.
	Tom, you have boards in your place?
A Man	Yes, Preacher.
Preacher	Bring six in the church,

	We may have use for them.
Gaby	So, Preacher, is all right to have the bongo?
Preacher	Yes. Bongo, my son,
	Bongo and be free,
	Is all that remain.
1st Man	The men want to see the Stranger dance.
Voices	Yes, we want to see the Stranger bongo!
Jeremy	(sizing up Stranger)
	You does bongo good?
Stranger	Better than most
	And no worse than the best.
Jeremy	You going dance tonight?
Stranger	In the ripeness of time.
Jeremy	You can't disappoint us, being a guest
	We raise this chorus especial for you.
	We hear you have fame and feel is best
	You give us a sample of what you can do.
	So bongo tonight, Stranger.
Stranger	When the time full.

(Old Woman pushes her way through crowd. She is
smothered in a blanket against the night. Preacher
goes to her.)

Preacher	Sarah, is you? The night air cold,
	Come let me conduct you back to your room,
	Dew falling heavy, it ain't good for the old———
Old Woman	I come to see the bongo-man dance.
	Which is the young man I see in my dream?
	(Crosses to Stranger.)
	Yes, ah yes, you favour my Sam.
	How old you is, boy? No more than nineteen,
	Stand up let me see; light as a fly,
	Nimble as a bee in search of a queen,
	You favour my Sammy, gone five months from me,
	Cut down like a cedar before he could flower,
	Crushed by a column of barbarous steel
	Loosened by envy to snatch him from me,
	The best bongo dancer the world ever see.
Voices	Jeremy Jordan is better than he!

Old Woman	Jeremy Jordan! that name is a stake
	Dug in my heart whenever it sound.
	Who drive the crane when it run amuck,
	Who foot on the pedal, who hand on the brake
	That couldn't control that monster of death?
	Jeremy Fumbler, fit for a rope,
	When he dance bongo, he commit a rape.
Jeremy	Old Woman, crooked with grief, go inside.
	Your heart is cracked, and crazy you speak.
	Sammy was my bosom friend, when he died
	Three days I couldn't dance, eat or sleep,
	Nearly, in truth, went out of my mind.
	But when it come to bongo, forgive me,
	Sammy was a babe, if even he live.
1st Man	Preacher, take Miss Sarah inside,
	The night air ain't good for she being old.
Preacher	Come, Sarah, come, together we'll talk
	And sing and dream about days long ago.
Old Woman	Preacher, I staying to watch the bongo.
Preacher	Then is my turn to leave, and leave a good night
	Blessing for all who need it tonight.
	Suffering Sarah, for your relief
	Long overdue from a well-run life.
	Blessing for you, Jeremy, whose young arm
	Belong as much to the power as you,
	The power that consumes like unquenchable fire.
	And to your father, Josiah, and friend,
	Faithful Obadiah, to you, and all
	Others, witness of what may befall,
	Blessing and good night from Preacher to you.
Several	Good night, Preacher, good night.
Preacher	And the cedar boards,
	Remember them, Tom.
Tom	Yes, Preacher, I will.
	(*Preacher goes into the church.*)
Jeremy	If the old talk finish, bongo can start.
	Stranger, join in whenever you want.
Stranger	I will dance when the time come,

When the bongo ripen with the drum,
Not soon or late, but when the time come.

Old Woman (*goes to Stranger*)
Sweet Stranger, dance for an old woman joy,
Dance one time and sweetly, my boy;
Dance and carry my old soul away
Floating between the night and the day;
Dance like a god descend from the sky
Tasting of freedom and not knowing why
The drums and the kwa-kwa capture his soul
When the heavenly chorus leave it cold;
Dance, my son, and put them to shame,
Dance for my grandson, Sammy, name!
(*She kisses Stranger and sits on her stool at edge of crowd. Stranger also sits.*)

1st Man
Start a chorus again. One man at a time
So the Stranger can pick his partner to dance.
(*Drum, kwa-kwa and voices blend.*)

Chantrelle & Chorus
Jeremy is the best o' we,
Cedarpost bongo!
Jeremy come bongo for me,
Cedarpost bongo!
Jeremy is a bird set free,
Cedarpost bongo!
Jeremy is a fish in the sea,
Cedarpost bongo!
Jeremy I love you, oui,
Cedarpost bongo!
Jeremy come stay with me,
Cedarpost bongo!
Jeremy, O Jeremy,
Cedarpost bongo!
Jeremy come sleep with me,
Cedarpost bongo!
(*One man dances a turn. Jeremy stops him. Drums softly in background.*)

Jeremy
Stranger, how you like the bongo?

Stranger
It coming to come.

Jeremy	You ready to dance?
Old Woman	The bongo still young,
	It ain't good enough.
	Try a next dancer.
	(*Music again. Second dancer. Jeremy stops him. Drums in background.*)
Jeremy	How the bongo this time?
Stranger	It ain't reach yet.
Jeremy	Good or bad you must dance.
	Come in the circle.
Stranger	In the ripeness of time.
Jeremy	Somebody else come do the bongo!
Old Woman	Dance yourself, Jeremy, don't frighten to dance.
	Fish in the sea, bird in the air,
	Sleeper with women, since you so good,
	Bongo, and tempt the Stranger to dance!
Jeremy	Start the chorus for me, and give it a zip.
	You have to dance, Stranger.
	(*Jeremy removes his shoes, rolls up his pants' legs, knots the tail-ends of his shirt round his middle. Chorus again and he begins to dance. He calls to Stranger to join him, but the latter shakes his head. Jeremy dances some more, furiously. Stranger again declines to join in. Old Woman begins high-pitched laughter. Jeremy stops and music, except for soft drums.*)
Old Woman	(*shrieking with laughter*)
	He ain't good enough for the Stranger to dance!
	Jeremy Clumsy, best in the land!
Jeremy	(*facing Stranger*)
	Now is your turn to dance.
	In the circle, bongo so all can see!
Stranger	The time ain't ripe.
Old Woman	(*dancing, taunting*)
	Jeremy Fumbler, fit for a rope!
Jeremy	(*striking Stranger*)
	Dance! god-damn you, bragger-man,
	Dance the bongo if you can!

Old Woman	(*dancing, taunting*)
	Jeremy Traitor, cut down a friend!
Stranger	So the end begin with a blow,
	And a sudden blow will summon the end,
	And then, at last, to dance the bongo.
	(*to Vendor*)
	Madam, I thirsty. An orange please
	Before I dance?
	(*Jeremy runs to tray, returns with orange and knife, cuts orange and gives to Stranger, holding knife. Stranger begins to suck the orange. Jeremy's impatience is at breaking point.*)
Jeremy	Hurry, Stranger, we can't wait no longer.
	Is your turn to dance.
Stranger	I dance for the dead.
Old Woman	Jeremy killer, cut down a friend!
	Best-in-the-land! dance at the end of a rope!
	(*She dances grotesquely before Jeremy, jeering at him. Jeremy plunges knife into her heart. She dies without a sound. The women kneel over her.*)
1st Man	(*to 2nd Man*)
	O God! he gone mad, my son gone mad
	Run quick for police.
2nd Man	A hanging in store
	For the village, that sure.
	(*He goes out.*)
Jeremy	(*unheeding the consternation around him*)
	You have your dead, Stranger,
	Dance now for the dead.
	Dance out here in the circle of light.
	Up with the drums and chorus last time
	We go see who is king bongo dancer tonight.

(*He strikes a pose. Stranger rises, crosses to centre of circle as drums, kwa-kwa and chorus rise. He removes his shoes, rolls up his trousers, knots the ends of his shirt and prepares to dance.*)

CURTAIN

34

Philip M. Sherlock

Born in Jamaica in 1902, Philip Sherlock is at present the Vice-Chancellor of the University of the West Indies. Formerly Head Master of Wolmer's School, he has been associated with the University of the West Indies since its inception, and was at one time Director of Extra-Mural Studies there.

Philip Sherlock has written many poems and essays, is the author of *Anansi the Spiderman*, a collection of Jamaican folk-tales. and co-author of *A Short History of the West Indies* (1956).

POCOMANIA

Long mountain, rise,
Lift you' shoulder, blot the moon,
Black the stars, hide the skies,
Long mountain, rise, lift you' shoulder high.

Black of skin and white of gown,
Black of night and candle light
White against the black of trees,
And altar white against the gloom,
Black of mountain high up there,
Long mountain, rise,
Lift you' shoulder, blot the moon,
Black the stars, black the sky.

Africa among the trees,
Asia with her mysteries,
Weaving white in flowing gown
Black long mountain looking down
Sees the shepherd and his flock
Dance and sing and wisdom mock
Dance and sing and falls away
All the civilized today

Dance and sing and fears let loose
Here the ancient gods that choose
Man for victim, man for hate,
Man for sacrifice to fate.

Hate and fear and madness black
Dance before the altar white.
Comes the circle closer still,
Shepherd weave your pattern old.
Africa among the trees
Asia with her mysteries.

Black of night and white of gown,
White of altar, black of trees,
Swing de circle wide again,
Fall an' cry, me sister, now.
Let de spirit come again,
Fling away de flesh and bone,
Let the spirit have a home.

Grunting low and in the dark
White of gown and circling dance
Gone today and all control,
Power of the past returns,
Africa among the trees,
Asia with her mysteries.

Black the stars, hide the sky,
Lift you' shoulders, blot the moon
Long Mountain, rise.

JAMAICAN FISHERMAN

Across the sand I saw a black man stride
    To fetch his fishing gear and broken things,
And silently that splendid body cried
    Its proud descent from ancient chiefs and kings.

Across the sand I saw him stride:
    Sang his black body in the sun's white light
The velvet coolness of dark forests wide,
    The blackness of the jungle's starless night.
He stood beside the old canoe which lay
Upon the beach; swept up within his arms
The broken nets and careless bounded away
Towards his wretched hut——
Nor knew how fiercely spoke his body then
Of ancient wealth and savage regal men.

John Hearne

Born in Jamaica in 1925, John Hearne is the most outstanding of living Jamaican novelists. His main works are *Stranger at the Gate* (1951), *Faces of Love* (1957) and *The Land of the Living* (1961). His novels have been translated into many languages.

John Hearne taught at Jamaica College, has worked for the Jamaica Broadcasting Corporation, and has lectured in the Extra-Mural Department of the University of the West Indies.

THE WIND IN THIS CORNER

In the middle of the morning we drove out of the low, scrubby Queenshaven Hills and into the Braganza plain. It was very hot and dry outside, but in the car, going fast with the windows open, the heat was only pleasant: a warm, thick-textured rush of air, smelling of baked brick and a peppery, grassy tang of the deep country. Charlie McIntosh was driving us in his car, the big, always dusty, hard-used Buick that had covered every road in Cayuna bigger than a bridle path; I was sitting behind with my forearms resting on the back rest of the driver's seat; and Roger Eliot sat beside Charlie.

"Well, it's a good day for it," Roger Eliot said.

"A good day for what?" Charlie McIntosh asked, before I could nudge him to keep quiet.

"A good day for murder," Roger told him. "I don't like committing murder in bad weather. That spoils everything. Don't you think so, Charlie?"

"Oh, God!" Charlie muttered. He was the older man but he sounded like a boy who has gone too far with adults and has been brutally snubbed. "You don't have to talk like that, Roger. It's not funny."

His florid, pleasant face was hurt and very Jewish, and as he squirmed in his seat, I felt the big car surge forward on a burst of new speed. Charlie always finds comfort and release, in any situation that seems to go beyond his grasp, by driving too fast, or by swimming furiously across harbours in which there are barracuda,

38

or by getting drunk in a dozen widely separated bars, driving too fast to each of them.

"How are the other assassins?" Roger said and turned to look back past me and through the rear window. "Good. They're still keeping up. We won't have to do all the knife work alone."

"It might help if you shut up, Roger," I told him. "None of us is going to enjoy what we have to do. So why not stop whining as if you're the only one who hates it?"

His small green eyes were sombre and forbidding as they turned to me, and his long, pale, ugly face was too vivid and yet empty. It reminded me of the sad, dangerous face you see, sometimes, when a man has been smoking *ganja* and feels all his connections with other men are down and is getting ready to kill or maim simply to assure himself that the gap he senses can be bridged. I made a fist and punched Roger gently on the shoulder and smiled. Sometimes people like Charlie and me, in the party, tend to forget how young Roger Eliot is. He is so good that it is easy to forget.

"Go on," I said. "I know what the Old Man means to you. But what about us, eh? You think we don't feel it too?" He made a wry, tired grimace of disgust and turned away and looked before him again. We were travelling through the cane fields now, but from the rear window I could still see the hills, close behind us and faded by the long dry season. They were a dusty grey-green, stark and inhospitable under the glowing sky. Where the road had been laid across the saddle there was a white gash of limestone looking strangely alive against the bleached-out dehydrated bush of the hill slope. The other cars were strung out along the straight road: Osbourne's Riley and Douglas's black Jaguar close together, and a good way behind, Dennis Broderick's old station waggon trailing a lot of dirty blue exhaust. The canes were all around us, close packed, tawny with the sun, stretching for ten miles down to the coast where the sky above the swamps was grey and hazy. The pink earth from the fields was dusted on the black road, and occasionally, as the tyres churned the soft surface, a tickling earth smell mingled with the sharpness of hot asphalt would swirl briefly about the car.

"Do we have time to stop for a drink at Sherwood Bridge?" Roger asked me.

"Sure," I said. "Do you need one?"

"Good God, yes, man, I don't want to go into him cold. Do you?"

"No," I agreed. "A drink would be a good idea. Get rid of this lead in my stomach. We don't want to get caught up in Sherwood Bridge, though. How long since you've been there?"

"About three months," Roger said. "When I was speaking at the Agricultural Show. But it's Charlie's territory. When were you over last, Charlie?"

"Ten days ago," Charlie told him. "There shouldn't be much to hold us up today. They won't have many new things that need listening to. Besides, it won't be a bad thing for Eugene to show his face. He's been so busy in the Eastmoreland divisions he hasn't had time for Braganza."

"How's he doing in Eastmoreland?" I asked. "Are we going to win down there?"

"You tell me," Charlie said. "Does anybody ever know how Eastmoreland is going to vote? Jesus, I'm glad I don't have to fight the election down there. Those Eastmoreland boys kiss you on Monday and hang you on Tuesday, and nobody ever knows why they do either."

"They're not the only ones," Roger said. His voice wasn't pleasant. It was flat and too precise and full of that angry sadness I had seen on his face. "When it comes to kissing and killing, we're doing all right, aren't we, Charlie?"

I saw Charlie's hands tighten on the wheel. He had big hands, firmly fleshed and virile like the rest of his body, covered with reddish freckles and a thick pelt of fine dark hairs. When he turned his face briefly to Roger, the full red lips were thinly compressed and the heavy bar of his moustache made a melancholy, decisive sweep across his profile.

"When we stop at Sherwood Bridge," he said, dead and even, "you can take the car and drive back to town. Tony and I will go on with Eugene. If you don't want to do this, then you can back out now. . . . I've had enough. You hear me?"

"Me too," I said. "I know Charlie and me and the rest of us are pretty coarse, Roger, compared with you, but just stop reminding us how sensitive you are, eh."

The strange thing about it was that I think we all knew what we were trying to do. We were trying to get angry with each other so that when we reached the Old Man there would be enough anger left for us to do the job properly.

"Oh, shut up, both of you," Roger said. He passed his hand roughly over his pallid, heat-shiny face. "Let me think what I'm going to say to him. You have any cigarettes left, Tony?"

"Sure," I said, and smiled at him as he turned round and took one from the packet. "Take it easy, boy. We've given you a nasty job, but take it easy."

"You want me to do it?" Charlie asked. "I'll do it, Roger. It ought to have been me from the beginning. Not you. It was a son-of-a-bitch trick asking you to tell him."

Roger looked at him sideways and gave a warm, harsh snort of laughter.

"You know something, Charlie," he said. "You're a nice old bastard. Only your mother and I know it, but you're all right. No. I'll do it. I have to."

"Let me do it," Charlie said. "It ought to come from me."

"Don't be damn' silly," Roger said. "Of course I have to do it. If you or Tony or Eugene, or any of the others, initiated this it would finish him. When he thinks of the party and the movement now, it's your faces he sees. All of you who were with him from the beginning, or who went to prison with him during the war. No, you couldn't do it. When I do it, I'll be speaking for the new guard, eh, for the hard young professionals who hope to govern this bloody island after the election. He'll understand that—just. I hope."

We drove on into the hot, sharp shadowed plain. Nobody wanted to say anything more. We had said it all too often before this Sunday morning, and no amount of talking had made it any easier.

At Sherwood Bridge we stopped beside the yellow, plastered wall of the Chinese grocery; when we climbed from the car and stood on the gritty pavement, the heat rose from the concrete and enfolded us. The water in the gutter ran slimy and tepid around the tyres of the Buick, and a bright dense glare was flung into our faces from the whitelimed wall of the courthouse across the street. The little town had the dreamy, suspended feeling of Sunday morning and a church bell somewhere sounded thin and lost in the still air. In about a minute the first people began to gather round us, and by the time the other cars turned into the street there was a good crowd on the pavement outside the grocery. If only half of them meant to vote for us, it was still good to see that so many had collected so quickly.

There was a lot of excitement when Eugene Douglas's grey lion head emerged from his car, and further excitement, but lesser, when Osbourne and Broderick pulled up. Listening to the voices, I realized that unless the party did something very foolish we were in this time. Even allowing for the fact that this was the Old Man's parish, there was a note of recognition and pleasure in the voices that I had been hearing now for the last two months in other districts. It came from something more than the Old Man's personal influence, and we all had waited a long time for that sound from a crowd.

We went from the pulsing heat of the pavement into the green, bottle-glimmering coolness of the bar. Yap, the grocer, was standing behind the scarred wooden counter and smiling as he saw the crowd coming after us. Everyone was talking at once and somebody put a glass into my hand and Yap looked at me, pointing to a bottle of soda on the counter, and I nodded and he opened it, and handed it to me over the shifting heads. I splashed a little into the drink I had been given and watched the dark amber of the rum turn to pale gold and gave the bottle into a hand that reached out from the crowd.

This was the sort of gathering in which you realized how good Roger Eliot was. As I talked to the people around me, I could see him in the middle of his group, very tall, white-faced, with that distinctive, bony ugliness, turning from man to man unhurriedly. Each response was certain and intimate and you knew that he enjoyed this campaigning in the grass roots as most men enjoy being with a pretty woman. This was his gift. One of his many. Charlie McIntosh had it too, by background training and because being with the crowd made him feel happy, but he would never have, in addition, the cold, legalistic authority that Roger could turn on in the House like the controlled, merciless bursts from a machine-gun. In the House, apart from the Old Man, the only person who carried more sheer weight was Eugene Douglas, and then only because he had more experience and had been with the Old Man from the very beginning. And nowadays when you sat in the visitors' gallery, facing the opposition benches, and saw Roger Eliot and Eugene Douglas lounging side by side, each with that bleakly exultant histrionic barrister's keenness on his face, you realized that Roger was the greater man. He was greater because he was younger and we had given him a party and a machine to inherit. Sometimes, I wondered if we had asked too much of him too soon. It seemed to me that a lot of youth and a lot of gentleness had vanished from that intense, tautly preoccupied face while none of us was really looking.

He began to tell a clever and destructive story about the government and even the men talking with Eugene stopped to listen. I had heard it before, but listening to him tell it I found myself grinning. It was all very personal and rather obscene, as stories like that tend to be in Cayuna. We all pretend to be outraged when we hear them against ourselves, and then we start digging up one about our opponents. When he had finished, the laughter crashed around us like surf.

"Den tell me, Mister Eliot," one of the men said; he looked like a cane worker or a small farmer, in for the day. "How we gwine do when election come? Who gwine win dis time?"

Roger grinned and pushed him roughly, like a father pushing a grown son with affection. Nobody else but Charlie or the Old Man could have done it in quite that way without patronage.

"Who gwine *win*?" he mocked the man, and appealed theatrically to the crowd. "Who gwine win? You hear him? We going to win, of course. How you can ask a damn' fool question like that, man? Lord, but we getting some milk an' water workers in the party nowadays. Who gwine win?"

He clapped the man on the shoulder, hard, and grinned down at him, enjoying what he was doing so genuinely that the man grinned too, with delight and confidence, as the rest had already begun to chuckle and repeat what Roger had said.

When it was time for us to go, the men in the bar came out to the pavement and watched us getting into the cars. They were very pleased that we were going on to see the Old Man, and they waved us down the street until we turned the corner by the Methodist Church.

Beyond the church there was an iron bridge spanning a shallow, dirty green river; sugar cane began on the far bank of the river and the great column of the sugar factory chimney towered red and harsh into the deep, soft sky. We could see the clean shimmers of heat rising from the road.

Two miles from Sherwood Bridge, Charlie turned the Buick into a pink, rocky side road, and as the big car lurched and jolted in the ruts, I could see, in the driving mirror, the others following. On the left there was a big, dried-out pasture with the Old Man's famous mules grazing on the dusty stubble, along with four lordly jacks and seven swollen mares. In the field on the left there was a stand of heavy maize and another of dense, cool-looking tobacco. Then the road began to rise a little and there, just under the crest of the hillock, was the Old Man's house, and the Old Man, who must have heard the cars, standing against a pillar at the head of his steps, lifting his hand as we drove into the yard and parked in the shade of a breadfruit tree.

"Well, gentlemen," he said, and came halfway down the steps to meet us. "What an unexpected pleasure. Charlie, you young scoundrel, I knew you were coming. But not everyone else."

The great, square, cropped head moved forward on the enormous neck as he squinted into the yard to where Eugene Douglas, Broderick and Osbourne were getting from their cars.

"Eugene!" he called as he took my hand and Roger's simultaneously. "I almost didn't recognize you. I thought you must have left the island. . . ."

"D.J.," said Eugene, and came up and put his hands on the Old Man's shoulders. "How are you? I've been out of town every time you've come up. Things are tight in Eastmoreland and All Souls. We're going to need you in both places before the election. If we don't get at least one set of seats from those two we might lose again."

"We'll get 'em," the Old Man said crisply. "I promise you that. We have to, eh. We can't lose this time. Twice is as much as anyone can afford to lose in Cayuna. After that you're bad luck."

He stood, still holding Eugene by the arms, and smiling at us with the slight half-twist of the lips that, for as long as we could remember, had always accompanied his brief, almost aphoristic lectures on the strategy of practical politics. Each of us there, except Roger Eliot, could have written down about two hundred sentences, nearly proverbs, with which for over thirty years the Old Man had taught all he had learnt.

"No, gentlemen," the Old Man continued. "We cannot lose this time. Do not even entertain the idea. Now let's go in and spend a proper Cayuna Sunday morning. Good heavens, but it's splendid to see you all like this."

He turned and led us up the broad steps: a short, bow-legged old man, with immense shoulders, and a back as broad as a bank door, who yet managed to appear of a height in a crowd of tall men. Always, in the past, when you had bent your head to talk to him you felt as if he were making the concession. And now, as I watched his stiff-collared, immaculately linen-suited figure between the bright-patterned, fluttering sports-shirts and casual slacks of Roger and Eugene, there was still enough of the old demonic authority left to make those two towering men appear somehow slight.

"Mildred!" The marvellous gong of a voice carried through the darkened, cool rooms of the old house. "Mildred, we have guests. Tell the girl to bring ice and all the rest of it. Come, gentlemen. Draw up your chairs here. The wind in this corner is always cool for some reason. Some accident of architecture. On the hottest day it's always pleasant here. I know how you Queenshaven people complain about our Braganza heat. It makes men, though. You need a furnace for a good sword."

Watching us as we drew the wicker chairs into a semi-circle on the broad, wooden veranda, his old, wildly seamed face was firm and glowing with happiness. The huge, deer-like eyes sparkled. Once those enormous, liquid eyes and that compactly massive, squat body had been very nearly irresistible. All over Cayuna, now, you could see men and women, of all colours, with those same sloping, heavy shoulders.

"D.J.," Charlie said, "you have any of that whisky you gave me when I was over last week? Jesus, but that was a whisky, man. Don't give it to these crows. They wouldn't appreciate it. Save it for you and me."

The Old Man laughed: an emphatic, musical bark. He glared

at Charlie with a furious love that became suddenly too naked to witness without embarrassment. From the beginning, he had respected Eugene and Osbourne as nearly his peers, or been fond of those like Broderick and myself, but it had been Charlie who filled his hunger for the legitimate son he had never been able to have. Now there was only his daughter: a grey, plump woman called Mildred; silent and distant like so many country spinsters.

"Any of that whisky?" the Old Man said. "Charlie McIntosh, you're a damned blackguard, as I've always maintained. Gentlemen, that person you see making himself at home on my veranda came here last week and under the pretence of talking party business filled his guts with over a quart of whisky I keep for important guests. . . . Mildred, for God's sake, child, where is the drink? You want these poor men to die of thirst?"

He raised his voice to an unconstrained shout, and rubbed his hands together as if crushing his pleasure to get its essence. Then, as the maid came out with the drinks and Mildred followed her, he sat down. We rose and Miss Mildred nodded to our greetings with a disdain that we knew was not directed at us personally but at whatever fate or chance had caused men to leave her alone with only a genially tyrannical old father to care for. She saw to the maid as the girl set the big mahoe tray with its load of bottles, glasses and a bowl of ice on the low veranda table. They both went inside again immediately. The maid was a big, clumsy-looking girl, not wearing shoes, so I knew she must be from far back in the country, probably from the St. Joseph mountains. She seemed to be very apprehensive of Miss Mildred.

"Now," said the Old Man. He was alight with anticipation. Talking and drinking were two of the four or five things he had always liked doing best. He took us all in with one quick, hot glance. "Charlie, my boy, work for your living. Find out what these gentlemen would like and give me a whisky and water. You know how I like it."

"Yes," Charlie said, under his breath. "Five fingers of liquor and the dew off a blade of grass."

"What's that? What did you say?"

"Nothing, D.J. Nothing. Just thinking aloud."

"I hope so. I hope that was all."

I felt the smile on my face become unbearably strained and looked at Roger desperately, begging him in my mind to say what he had come to say and stop this ritual exchange between Charlie and the Old Man. Roger was carefully mixing himself a rum and ginger-ale, not waiting for Charlie to help him, and not looking at anybody. You could sense the crushing, Braganza heat in the bright yard, but the wind in this corner of the veranda was cool and gentle. As the Old Man had said it would be. As I had known it would be. I had sat here often enough. After a long time Charlie gave me my drink.

"Here's to victory, D.J.," I said, and lifted my glass.

"I'll drink to that, Tony." He smiled, raising his glass first to me and then to the others, and then ran his square-tipped, coffee-brown fingers energetically through the cropped, silver lawn of his hair. "My God, I'll drink to that. It's been a long time, eh? Thirty years. You boys were in your twenties. And Roger ... were you born yet, Roger?"

"Yes," Roger told him. "I was born. I wasn't taking much notice, you understand, but I was born."

"My God," the Old Man said again. "Sometimes it seems like thirty centuries and sometimes like thirty months. I used to think I was mad sometimes. Expecting this damned island to want independence. You remember what they called us then? 'The black man's party.' Well, if we never win an election we can be proud of that. There isn't a politician in the island now who wouldn't like to have that title for his party. That's our doing."

"You know what the government boys have started calling us these days?" Eugene asked him.

"No, what?"

"The white man's party. I heard Gomez saying that over in Eastmoreland the other day."

The Old Man threw his head against the back of his chair and laughed. The wickerwork gave that peculiar shushing creak of straw as the chair shook under him.

"Why?" he asked, and chuckled again. "Why?"

"Oh, because of Roger, I suppose. Charlie too, if you count Jews. Mostly because Fabricus is standing in Eastmoreland and is being very popular. It's his old parish, you know? Before he came to Queenshaven. He's beginning to frighten the government now, so Gomez decided to use his colour against him."

"Lack of colour, you mean," the Old Man said with delight. "Good. That's what I like to hear. Black man's party. White man's party. Jew man's party. Chinaman's party. They'll soon run out of labels. Each time they clap another one on us, it means we're hurting them somewhere."

"We've got them running, all right," Charlie said, "but it's going to be close. They could edge us out yet."

"Close!" the Old Man said. "Of course it's going to be close. But it's our election. I can smell it. If we get in this time, and the next, we're set for a long innings. Good God! After thirty years' fighting, to sit with men like you on a government front bench."

He leaned forward and gave his empty glass to Charlie. The stretched, deeply grooved skin of his face was burnished with the drink he had just taken. Charlie mixed him another quickly and he leaned back again. The long stomach was quite flat under the gleaming starched linen waistcoat, and in the irreducible, worn bronze of his face, the eyes were much too young and adventurous.

Now, I said to myself, now, Roger. He's given you the cue. Say what you have to say. For all of us. If you don't say it now, when will you ever say it?

I heard the shallow heave of Eugene's breathing beside me. Broderick's fat yellow face was beaded with little unattractive drops of sweat. Charlie was a still, untidy heap in his chair, and Osbourne had begun to finish his drink in small, ridiculous sips.

"Look, D.J.," Roger said. "We haven't come out just to finish your liquor. We want to talk a few things over with you. Election business. And about afterwards."

His precise and resonant lawyer's voice was a little high. He looked into his drink, swallowed half of it.

"Of course," the Old Man said. "I have a number of points I want to raise myself. I shall be putting them before the executive, officially, when we meet in Queenshaven next week, but so many of you are here this morning that I'd like to discuss them now."

"What we had in mind——" Roger said.

"I made a memorandum," the Old Man said. "Mildred was typing it for me last night. I'll go and get it. . . . Gentlemen, your

48

glasses are empty. Charlie McIntosh, you dog, see to your duties or I'll cut you off with a shilling."

He stood up and his stiffness in getting from the chair was barely perceptible. And then we were looking at each other and listening to the slow, decisive footsteps going across the wooden floor of the old-fashioned drawing-room.

"He never even listened," Roger said. "Has he ever listened? He's run this damned party so long he thinks it's his personal property. There's no easy way out of it now, Eugene. I'm going to give it to him straight. He won't understand it otherwise."

"He *was* the party," Broderick said sullenly. "He was all the party this island had when you were still wetting your pants, Roger. When I was half your age, he was burning up Cayuna like a bush fire. He has a right to say his say. More right than any of us. My God!"

Roger turned on him with the speed of a biting dog, and I could almost touch the relief and eagerness with which he fastened on a cause for anger. On the excuse for any heat that might drive him through what he had to tell the Old Man.

"Right, Broderick," he said. "You do it. Or don't let's do it. Just as you all please. Say the word, gentlemen, and I'll stop where I started and we'll listen to what he has to say, as we always have . . ."

He was shaking with desolate rage.

"We'll listen," Eugene said quietly. "We'll listen as we always have. And then we'll learn something, as we always have. But not until you've told him he can't stand for election again, Roger. Not until you've told him that he has to leave the House. That's what we came out here for, and you are going to do it, aren't you?"

"Yes," Roger said, and the word was rough with the violence of his conflict. "Yes, I'm going to tell him what he should have realized for himself. But I don't want any of you old comrades-in-arms looking at me as if it's all my idea."

"Nobody is doing that," Charlie said heavily. "Just do what you have to and get it over. It's going to be kinder that way."

Then we heard the Old Man's emphatic footfall coming back across the drawing-room. He stood in the doorway studying two closely typed pages of foolscap, his rolled-gold spectacles pushed up on his forehead. God knows why the Old Man had ever worn spectacles. His vision hadn't altered much between seven and seventy-five. But he wouldn't read the posters on a wall without an elaborate performance of taking out the ancient, faded, almost colourless, morocco case, removing the spectacles, putting them on carefully, and then, as carefully, pushing them up his forehead, almost to the hairline. This had become part of his legend. Cartoonists used it. Little, barefoot boys in the street acted it. Visitors to the House stayed to see it. It hadn't done us any harm at all.

"Gentlemen," the Old Man said, "I was considering our tactics the other night." Still studying his sheets he stepped on to the veranda and settled in his chair with a grunt. "I feel that we are going to need more emphasis in the north. Much more than we've given it up to now. It has always been our weak spot and we've always dodged it. Not any more though, gentlemen. We're going to take the fight to them——"

"D.J.," Roger said; his voice calm now, and weary, but suddenly assured. As he sat there, leaning forward with his elbows on his knees and holding his glass in both hands, I could see two hectic smears of colour along the cheek-bones, beneath the very pale, normally waxen skin. "D.J., before you get on to the general plan of the campaign, there is something we'd like to discuss. It's very important."

The Old Man looked up, the frowning flicker of his impatience merely suggested within the lustrous vitality of his eyes, like the lightning you thought you saw behind the mountains at night. "Certainly," he said to Roger. "We have all day. You're all staying to lunch, by the way. I've told Mildred. What's up, Roger? You sound worried." He sprawled easily, in that long familiar slouch of confident readiness, his face tightening into a still, sharply edged cast of experienced attention, the face of an old hunter to whom any problem is a repetition of one known long ago and yet one needing care because some detail is always new. "Elections!" he said happily. "They always bring more trouble than any blasted thing I know. Even women. They're the price we pay for being politicians."

"D.J.," Roger asked, "have you ever thought of giving up the House? Giving up parliamentary work, I mean, and using yourself on the trade union side?"

"Giving up the House?" We sat in a sort of hypnotized absorption as we watched bewilderment and then exasperated dismissal of an unworthy waste of time struggle for place in the Old Man. "Roger, boy, what the hell are you talking about? If that's what's on your mind, I'll settle it right away. No. I've never thought of leaving the House." He gave a short bark of laughter, half annoyed, half indulgent. "Not until the people of Braganza parish vote me out, at least. And they've been sending me up for thirty years now. What in God's name brought this on?"

"You," Roger said. "And the elections. And thinking about you after the elections."

"And what I'd be doing in trade union work at my age," the Old Man said, ignoring him still with the same wry anger that was no more than the quick reflex of a stallion at stud, "I don't know. What's the matter, had Brod been neglecting his duties there?" He winked at Broderick, who was the leader of the trade union congress that during the years had grown into affiliation with the party, and Broderick grimaced back at him stiffly as Roger got to his feet. He stood deliberately, and the three steps he made along the veranda and the three steps back were deliberate also, controlled and almost pensive, and when he stood above the Old Man, I thought, "Merciful Heavens, he looks just like the Old Man did that afternoon during the war when they came to arrest him for sedition as he left the House." And it was true. Roger as he stood there, elongated rather than merely tall, grotesquely thin, hunched in his bright shirt like a harlequin in the mime, all knobs, angles and elbows, with his tapered yet ugly hands jammed into his trouser pockets, was invested with the same moment's quality that I had seen on the Old Man when they arrested him, politely enough and on the steps outside because members were immune while the House sat: a quality at once angry and serene, dispassionately implacable with the sense of utter conviction.

"D.J.," Roger said. "Will you listen?" And the Old Man looked up quickly, as the weight of that charged voice roused in him his first serious apprehension.

"Yes," the Old Man said. "Go ahead, Roger."

"We're asking you to resign your seat," Roger said. "To resign and not make it an official executive matter. We want you to join

Broderick in the trade unions and do the sort of field work you still do better than anyone else. The executive want you to present them with your resignation when you come up next week."

"The executive," the Old Man said. "I didn't know the executive . . ." His voice had become thick and uncertain and when I saw the papers in his hand begin to shake I looked away. I didn't want to look at the others. "The executive," the Old Man said again, and then harshly, astonishment, not protest, but stark incomprehension, lending strength to the uncertain voice, "Why? I must have a reason for this." The great eyes as they stared at Roger were dulled, opaque and absolutely still and his face had a livid rigidity, as if he had gone beyond a point of disbelief to where the personal shock was much less than a sense of awed encounter with some fathomless and abstract phenomenon. "Why?" he demanded.

"Because we are going to win this time," Roger said, "and you could not stand five years as chief minister. No, listen, D.J. Let me finish." He was pleading and almost anxious now, hurrying what he could into the destruction we had chosen him to commit. "Do you have any idea what we're going to have to do in the next five years, after we get in? What sort of mess we have to clear up? There's five hours' paper work a night for any minister. Let alone the business in the House during the day. Half the year we'll be beating around Europe and America raising capital investment. Off one damn' plane, into another, living out of suitcases, fighting it out at all-day conferences for an extra million dollars. Do you really think you could do that, D.J.?"

The Old Man's gesture was unthinkably distant and disinterested.

"I believe," he said conversationally, almost absently, "that I have proved my capacity for work in the past. Go on. I should like to hear this to the end."

His gaze travelled to each of us, with a flat, bleak absence of surprise that was far worse than recognition of treachery. It was then, I think, that necessary, hungrily sought anger that had eluded Roger all morning finally seized him.

"Listen!" he shouted. "Listen, D.J." Not pleading and anxious now, but shivering in an ecstasy of inextricable rage and sadness. "You can't do it. You know you can't do it. However much you want to. It's a government you'll have to lead in October, not a radical opposition. You'd last a year, maybe two, and then you'd have to go. And even then you wouldn't have done your work properly. Well, we're not going to waste you like that, you hear. What you started in this island and what you built with us is too good to throw away. We want to use you where you'll do a job on the sugar estates or on the wharves, and among the fishermen. That's what you know. That's what you can do standing on your head. Tell me that isn't so. Tell me that isn't so, if you dare."

"I don't agree," the Old Man said.

"You don't agree." It was hard to tell whether the rasp in Roger's voice was savagery or tears or triumph. "Of course you don't agree. Not now. You want to be on the front bench with us. That's what you saw thirty years ago. A front bench with men like Eugene and Charlie and Tony and me. Well, you've got it for us. But it's not for you. And you'll know tomorrow. You probably know it already because that's the sort of man you are. If you weren't, do you think I'd be standing on this blasted veranda saying what I've just had to say?"

He was bent over, folded from the waist in that slightly incredible fashion of the immensely tall whose skeletons seem to struggle for release from the too scanty flesh, as if he were not bent but suspended from the ceiling by a wire attached to the base of his spine; his face, thrust close to the Old Man's, suffused now with the uncontainable mixture of sadness and pure fury, compelling from the Old Man, now, by some sheerly visible, silent and terrific explosion of will, an acknowledgement not only of those truths by which he had taught us to live in our work but of how well he had taught those truths to us, both men locked and isolated within that explosion of shared service, love and integrity of purpose, neither man conceding one particle of his anger or sorrow or stubborn righteousness until reluctantly, tentatively, then with sudden and prodigal generosity, the will of the older man recognized the faith behind the will of the younger, recognized that and saluted, also, what it must have cost a man as yet so young and vulnerable.

"Good God, boy," the Old Man said softly, "don't stand there like that. I feel as if you're a tree about to fall on me. Sit down."

Roger sat, in the slow careful fashion of a man who has been exhausted to a point where he dare not trust his muscles to perform the simplest action. As slowly he took his right hand and a handkerchief from his pocket and wiped the film of damp and grease from his face. He grinned lopsidedly at the Old Man. It was a hot day. Such as you get only in Braganza. In the middle of the cane fields, on the south side of the mountains, cut off from the northern trades and too far from the sea to catch the breeze. Even in this corner of the Old Man's veranda you could feel a declaration of heat, distinct and independent, parasitically attached to the accidental current of cool air.

"I did not realize," the Old Man said, "that this was the feeling of the executive. Of course I shall be proud to accept whatever you may suggest. Gentlemen! Your glasses are empty again. There is plenty of time for another before lunch. Charlie!"

His gaze, withdrawn but courteous, roved across our circle, not so much repudiating contact as, for now, impervious to what might mistakenly be offered as a substitute. Passed round us until it rested on Roger where he sat wrapped in his own exhaustion like a Mexican in his blanket.

Hot, I thought, dry hot. No rain. Much more of this and the Old Man will have to buy grass from the hills for his mules and his jacks and those mares in foal.

I don't know why this occurred to me then. Perhaps to protect me from an act of intimacy we had all witnessed, but from which all but two of us had been excluded.

Michael G. Smith

Like George Campbell, M. G. Smith was closely associated with the magazine *Focus* and the Jamaican independence movement. Many of his poems are metaphysical in tone, although his philosophizing is essentially poetic. His poetry is characterized by a highly emotional 'statement' of his feelings. However, he is better known as an anthropologist than as a poet.

Formerly a lecturer in the University of the West Indies, M. G. Smith now lives and teaches in the U.S.A.

JAMAICA

I saw my land in the morning
And O but she was fair
The hills flamed upwards scorning
Death and Failure here.

I saw through the mists of morning
A wave like a sea set free
Faith to the dawn returning
Dark tide bright unity.

I saw my friends in the morning
They called from an equal gate
"Build now: whilst time is burning
Forward before it's late."

The old Gods awake
    Past and Future break
    On as the voices roll
    Move as a single whole
    Forward
    Forward
    Forward
    O country to your goal.

Eric Roach

Eric Roach, who was born in Tobago in 1904, is the leading poet in Trinidad and Tobago. He is a regular contributor to *B.I.M.* published by Frank Collymore in Barbados. His poem *Homestead* was judged the best out of twenty-six submitted for the birthday contest of the Readers and Writers Guild of Trinidad and Tobago. Eric Roach is feature writer for the *Evening News*, Trinidad.

THE PICTURE

I would I were Rembrandt, had all that light,
My art his art, my paper for his canvas,
And see her so, to hold ever so,
A moment laughing in the running moment.

The wind turns gently through her rust-brown hair
And channels in her hollow cheek; her eyes
Alive with pleasure that her red mouth laughs;
A gesture like a phrase, a chord, a curve.

I would take care to show her in her world
That scorns and envies and outlaws her worth,
The freedom she must live, the gaiety she is,
The whole earth's love and pity she possesses.

I should take care to name the picture 'Harlot',
Lest those who come, not knowing, but enraptured
By the wild beauty and the goddess gesture
Should say she was the duchess of my heart.

It would not be the first time or the last
The truth were wronged nor the lie hidden in
The line or colour; the man must love the model,
Or the work comes stillborn from the soul.

Light rises in the mind; it filled Rembrandt's
And warmed him till he died. All that he looked at
Lives; all that he made burns like the sun:
Time cannot blind the vision of his spirit.

Time cannot burn the lovely legends down;
Their golden flame warms history's sodden heart.
Why, all that love and pity had Isolde,
And such a beauty had the Magdalen.

Ernest A. Carr

Born in Trinidad, Ernest Carr started his literary career by writing poetry which was published mainly in Caribbean literary journals. He has written about fifty stories, nearly all of which have been published. Twenty or more have been broadcast by the B.B.C. Ernest Carr has published various articles and essays in the Caribbean and in Canada.

CIVIL STRIFE

"Dick, I'm terribly worried over Syd," Ursula Bayson said. Her husband looked up from a catalogue of garden flowers and saw an orange tinge touching the pale yellow over her high cheek-bones and, flickering in her large, grey eyes, the chronic fear he always vaguely noted there. It seemed to have become more pronounced since they came back to live in the district where Ursula was born. To him, somehow, it exaggerated everything his wife said or did when she was dealing with her own people, the coloured folk of Sambury.

"Syd is so backward at school——" She paused, looking down and driving a few vindictive stitches in the side of socks she was mending. He expected a complaint about the little, 'black' boy over the way. She always started like this. It now came with a passion that heightened an elusive quality of her face, framed in a thundercloud of frizzly hair, that from their first acquaintance had held him.

"... Every second word from Syd is about that little, black boaster, what he says or does. I'm afraid Syd is growing to look up to him.... And how he's gone up a form in school and left Syd behind." There was a bitterness in her voice, and Dick could see the hardly controlled quivering of her lips.

This harping emphasis on 'black' was farcical and diverting, he always felt. But he was beginning to see—only just—after years, that it was not as harmless as he had supposed. He was white, and had known the humiliation and bitterness of class distinction and economic levels in his homeland. Now he found a shade of colour in Sambury, of all places, as substantial and formidable as those barriers.

"Syd may catch up with him in time, Ursie," he said quietly, resting a decisive finger on the flower-plate in the catalogue. "Syd's only ten. Give him a chance."

"I'm not so sure, Dick. We can't afford to take chances. I don't want our child bossed by that boy or others like him when he grows up." Her eyes darkened with concern. "Syd has it in him, of course. But he's so careless with everything. Lacks pride. Our child must not be left to be a laggard here. What about getting him a private tutor, Dick?"

Her husband closed the catalogue, keeping a finger between the pages. That faint smile she knew so well, telling of a body frail and a spirit gentle, unlike her robust strength and primitive energy, wandered over his intensely pale face to concentrate its warmth in his deep blue eyes. She had been bringing up this subject for the past week. He didn't think their son was backward at all. Syd was the kind of boy that takes to outdoor games and likes to be in the company of small boys like himself. He had tried without success to make her see. Even before the holidays started Syd had been taken up with jumping over a bar or across a pit in the backyard in preparation for the annual school sports. Syd was easygoing like him, she used to say, but did not possess quite his 'advantage'.

"I've spoken to the college Principal and he has recommended a young chap not long out of college," Dick said. "He's clever with small boys. Gets under their skin, Findlay assured me."

"You have, really?" Ursula cried with a girlish delight, her face glowing with a rich cyp colour. "O Dick, that's grand. Why didn't you tell me before? You know how anxious I am that Syd shouldn't lag behind, especially here in Sambury where the people are so rude and forward. Want to rub themselves against you. You know what I mean, Dick?" She took a deep breath, her eyes probing him for understanding and sympathy.

"I know. But why shouldn't they——" The subject tired him. Considerate as she was in other matters, she was ruthless with a seething fear in this. "Why take things so devilishly serious, Ursula?"

"Everybody here is so uppish and overbearing. They want to treat me as if I am one of them. Just one of them! They say I'm coloured. But I am not like them." A faint scorn played about her lips. "They are envious, I know, because I'm married to you."

"No! . . . I could never think that." He laughed, his blue eyes twinkling. "What's so precious about me, Ursie?"

"Am I like them, Dick?" There was a compelling earnestness in the depths of her wide, luminous eyes.

He now thought of the many people he had seen in Sambury so like her, at least in appearance. Glowing eyes, full, luscious lips, bodies vital and sensuous with the sun's ripening touch, he had admired, a little enviously, too. Faces in a crowd here stirred him in the golden sunlight as faces under a cold, northern sky had never done. And he was strangely reluctant to ask himself why. Sometimes when he looked out of a window he would exclaim with a delight—similar to Ursula's when she caught the blue of the sky mirrored in his eyes—that he saw framed a canvas painted by a Master achieving unity in variety. Just as he was trying to do with the native flowers and decorative plants of the island.

"Am I like them, Dick?" His wife's breathless insistence awoke him from the reverie.

"I find your people lovable, Ursie," he said with a gentle evasiveness, trying to be calming and reassuring.

"My people?" she exclaimed, and he saw a momentary startled look in her eyes which he thought he understood, for she had openly disavowed kinship with the 'Molasses skin' of Sambury.

"Yes, dear; you are lovable; but far more than anyone else." He held out a hand to her and laughed outright, to hide his puzzlement after eleven years of married life with this complex creature who bore, it seemed, a sensitive spot on every layer of her skin.

She left her seat and came and threw an arm round his neck. In her middle thirties, Ursula Bayson was still girlish and childishly romantic. Dick savoured an exquisite solace in her that way; and from their long intimacy he had become aware that much of her experience—that which kept moulding her maturity—had been modelled on things second-hand and coloured by an imagination that had never taken root in her native environment. At first, her pride in this had surprised him, but eventually it gained his tolerance. He had realized, with a secret satisfaction, that he was the reality her vagrant imagination had sought and found.

Her avid eyes now followed the line where her dusky skin met the white skin of his neck. He looked up and saw a smiling rapture on her face and knew she wanted to say something sentimental about things 'lilywhite', as she usually qualified them. She, too, caught in his eyes the quizzical amusement with which he often greeted her childish interest in certain of his physical features, and hesitated. For with it she sensed the impatience that once led him to tell her that much of what she delighted in was the result of his chronic invalidism which had driven him to seek the light and air and warmth of the Caribbean.

He drew her down to him and kissed her. He was grateful for her homage and devotion which he craved. He admitted he was a romantic himself, in a way. He felt that that was the real bond which united them. She didn't know, he mused sometimes, how beautiful he thought her in her native setting, and how he loved the things of her that indirectly she was so apologetic for.

"If you were stronger, Dick, we could go and live in England," she said wistfully, smoothing his thin, sandy hair and fondling the blue veins along his chalk-white temples.

"Go and live in England?" he said after a short silence. "Go away from this beautiful country where you had the good fortune to be born? This corner of life and laughter, stirring the blood like the dancing colours on the humming-bird's wing?" She saw a shadow fall over his face. "I've never enjoyed health until I came out here. Besides——" He passed an uncertain hand across his brow. "My father was a miner, I think I told you, Ursie. Sheer luck got me out of the groove."

He got up, holding the catalogue open. "I've found an interest here I couldn't possibly have had in England." They went to the window. "Have a look at my garden . . . see your native flower in the bed yonder?" He spread the catalogue on the sill, a finger on a coloured plate, and as Ursula turned her head to look at him again he said with an enthusiasm that brought a crimson flush to his face, "I think it far more lovely than this."

But Ursula tore her attention from the catalogue to stare over the garden. Her shoulder touched his, and he felt the tremor of vexed impatience that rose from the curve of her bosom to her firm chin and glittering eyes.

The boy who had incurred her uncontrollable dislike was standing in front of the gate leading to the garden. He was talking to Syd who leaned against a pillar, listening with an air of docile agreement. He was the dark colour of polished saman wood. His eyes, large and bright, rolled from Syd to surrounding objects, seeming to be taking everything with rapid, roving glances. His arms were akimbo, and Dick had the impression that he was listening and speaking at the same time, and that at any moment he would leap like a deer and be away. Occasionally he lifted a hand from his side to gesticulate as if to make a point with a striking self-assurance. Dick felt an instinctive liking for the little fellow.

Ursula moved away abruptly from the window and went to the front door. "Syd! Syd! Come in here at once!" she called. At the sound of her voice the boy darted down the street.

Dick went up to his wife, that quiet, quizzical look, so changeful, yet always gentle, baffling her, on his peaked face. "Ursie," he said, "why didn't you leave them alone? There're enough fighting cocks in the world already. Don't you think?"

About a week afterwards Maria, a girl of Portuguese extraction Mrs. Bayson had made a special journey to an orphanage out of the district to engage as maid, said to her, "Madam, a man out there. He says he wants to speak to you."

Ursula turned from slicing a grapefruit for Dick's lunch. "A man? What does he want?"

"Don't know, Ma'am. Just says he wants to speak to the 'Madam', if she's in."

"What sort of man, Maria?"

"A black man, Ma'am."

Ursula Bayson stiffened, something hard and unrelenting shone out of her eyes, scaring Maria as on the day her mistress caught her giggling with the 'black' postman over the fence. "Tell him he's come to the wrong house."

Maria came back, pale with apprehension, and said, "He won't go away, Ma'am. Says this is the house. Mr. Bayson sent the address. He's the teacher to teach Mr. Sydney, Ma'am."

Ursula flung the knife aside as she got up, a bristling hospitality in her every movement. "Black! ... Black! ... Black!" Maria heard her muttering huskily until she got to the front door.

On the veranda she saw a tall youth with a book under an arm. She took in that he had outgrown his clothes. He looked as one of the many indigent young men about Sambury. Over ambitious, over zealous, straining beyond their reach, she thought; and not prepared to take "No", however often it might be said. Out to learn things they shouldn't, and become doctors and lawyers and think themselves as good as men like Dick, and their sisters and mothers forgetting themselves when dealing with a woman like her.

His brown and very bright eyes greeted her, she thought, with an impudent familiarity, though he bowed, standing several feet away. "Good morning, Madam." His voice was hesitant and low.

She did not reply. And he saw the stony stare in forbidding eyes and the orange tinge over outraged cheeks. He fidgeted a moment and spoke again: "Dr. Findlay of King's College has arranged with Mr. Bayson—I was told he lives here—for me to give his son lessons three times a week." He straightened himself, the shy expectancy on his smooth, round, almost blue-black face straining her impatience to breaking point.

"Mr. Bayson is not at home," she rapped out. He looked away from the astringent lines about her mouth.

She had half turned to go back inside when he said, "Thank you, Madam. Everything is settled. I called only to introduce myself to the little fellow. He and I will be friends, Madam." The faint smile, ingenuous and as enigmatic as Dick's could sometimes be, which now touched his face, sent her gorge up. She watched him through half-closed eyes as he went down the steps. He paused to look at her husband's flower-beds before going out of the gate.

Anthony Christophe, the young tutor, started Syd on his lessons. Dick could feel the tension in his wife while the tutor was in the house, even though the room in which the lessons were given was right at the back. When she saw how well he and Syd got on, she became at times unreasonably harsh to Syd himself, Dick thought.

"That man comes into the place as if he owns it," she said to Dick a week after Christophe came. "Doesn't even want to open his mouth to say 'Good afternoon' when he sees me or Maria."

"Perhaps he feels you don't want him to," Dick returned in a neutral tone. "I was like that myself when I was a lad." He smiled at the furious look she gave him and went and rested a hand on her head.

"I hate this 'Mr. Christophe', 'Mr. Christophe' always coming from Syd," she said tensely, clenching her fine teeth. "He's worshipping the man, not learning his lessons."

"Come now, Ursie," Dick said, straining her black, clinging hair through his anaemic fingers, "tell me what it is you object to about this young man. His behaviour, colour of skin or his name?"

"I like neither," she snapped. "And his name reminds me too much of black people as slaves. . . ."

"Well, well, well!" exclaimed Dick with one of his sudden bursts of laughter. "I didn't think it was as bad as all that, Ursie."

She was still regarding him, puzzled, when voices came to them from the garden. Ursula got up and looked out.

"What does he mean by interfering with your plants, Dick?" she said excitedly, beckoning her husband with her long, nervous fingers.

"I've always told you so, Dick," she pattered energetically as he came to her side. "Forward, interfering, overbearing. They don't know their places. That man is one of them."

Dick felt the burning spite in her words as he peered through the window. He saw the young tutor pat Syd lightly on the shoulder and go out the gate. Syd turned and came into the house.

"Syd, what were you doing to your father's flower-beds?" she demanded. "You know he doesn't like anyone spoiling what he has done."

"Oh, I'm doing botany in class, mother," Syd said proudly. "And Mr. Christophe was showing me the cotyledon of a seed growing in one of the beds."

"Good at botany, too, is he, eh?" Dick remarked with evident pleasure. "I must ask him a few questions about some seeds I find hard to germinate. You know the definitions of that word, I hope, my boy." And he caught Syd's face between his hands, laughing, for he thought he saw, for the first time, a charge of treason in his wife's shocked stare.

64

Dick Bayson's garden was a dazzling blaze of colours in the afternoon sun a fortnight later. In the showering gold of August with the white-fire dance on the emerald of Sambury Hill, the garden had caught the hues and shimmering sheen of the humming-birds that came down to it. It was the object of admiring comments.

"You don't mind my taking your picture?" a man with a camera addressed both Syd and his tutor. They were standing just within the front gate. "I want a snap of this garden," the man added. "I understand every plant in it belongs to the island."

Before they had fully grasped what he was about, he had motioned them into position. Mrs. Bayson was attracted by the voices and came out on to the veranda, from sheer curiosity she later told her husband. And just then the camera clicked, the man lowered it, nodded amicably and walked briskly away.

It must have been about a week after this that Ursula opened the door of Dick's workroom and slammed it behind her so violently that he gave a nervous start and swung round. It was not like her to do this; she had always been careful to do nothing that might affect his delicate health. Her storm-cloud hair was now unravelled as by a gale; her face a dark, olive tint. She threw an illustrated weekly paper on to the table, scattering the seeds he had been sorting.

"When was this taken, Ursie?" He caught his breath at the photograph of his garden in a riot of glorious colours.

She ignored the question. "Do you recognize the people in it?" she asked, and he heard the hiss of her indrawn breath.

"Yes, I see you ... and Syd ... and ... Mr. Christophe!" She jabbed a finger pointed with steel at some words below. He read : " 'A native family in a native setting'."

Well, he had to do it. For Ursula's peace of mind; to restore Syd's relationship with his mother; and for his nerves as well. The arrangement with Anthony Christophe was terminated. But what had finally driven him to act quickly was something his wife had told him.

"Dick," Ursula had said, her eyes like those of a frightened child, appealing to him for protection and comfort, "this man, Syd's tutor, has thrown a black cloud about the house. It is covering me! And when I close my eyes I keep seeing a face, black as midnight, and with the white of the balls of the eyes peering at me, mocking me, making faces and coming closer to——"

He discovered that this was an exact description of a picture in a book his wife had seen and been terrified of as a child in Sambury. And in an excess of sympathy that had drowned his astonishment, he confided to her that he, too, slept on a cushion of memories. One of them was a now vague experience of a coal-mine when he was a child in England. The years had thinned the grim shadow, but a shiver still ran through him when his home town was named.

Then a fortnight after Anthony Christophe had gone, Dick Bayson received a letter. He sighed. Life could be so beautiful, in the golden light of the sunlight, as he felt it, yet so faithless; like a lovely woman, led astray to become the plaything of blind, mysterious forces cruelly besmirching her name.

He read: "Thank you ever so much, Mr. Bayson. My nephew tells me how kind you were to him. I must tell you that your recommendation has enabled him to obtain a very good position which, I feel sure, will help him to realise his ambition.

"I have not had the honour and pleasure to meet your lady. But I beg that you convey to her my sincere respect. My grandmother used often to speak to her. She knew her as a baby, before her mother, who was our grandmother's last and favourite daughter, left Sambury. I can assure you, Sir, the Christophes are a very old and respected family."

It was signed '(Miss) Lenore Christophe,

Head Mistress, Caribbean High School.'

Derek A. Walcott

Derek Walcott was born in St. Lucia in 1930 and began to write and be published at a very early age. Some of his more important works to date are: *Twenty-five Poems* (Trinidad 1948), *In a Green Night, Poems 1948–1960* (London 1962). He is also the author of a number of plays: *The Sea at Dauphin* (Jamaica 1954), and *Henri Christophe.*

A CAREFUL PASSION

Hosanna, I build me house, Lawd,
De rain come wash it 'way.

Jamaican Song

The Cruise Inn, at the city's edge,
Extends a breezy prospect of the sea
From tables fixed like islands near a hedge
Of foam-white flowers, and to deaden thought,
Marimba medleys from a local band,
To whose gay peace my love now drummed a hand.
I watched an old Greek freighter quitting port.

You hardly smell the salt breeze in this country
Except you come down to the harbour's edge
Not like the smaller islands to the south.
There the green wave spreads on the printless beach.
I think of wet hair and a grape red mouth.
The hand which wears her husband's ring, lies
On the table idly, a brown leaf on the sand.
The other brushes off two coupling flies.
"Sometimes I wonder if you've lost your speech."
Above our heads, the rusty cries
Of gulls revolving in the wind.
Wave after wave of memory silts the mind.

The gulls seem happy in their element.
We are lapped gently in the sentiment
Of a small table by the harbour's edge.
Hearts learn to die well that have died before.
My sun-puffed carcass, its eyes full of sand,
Rolls, spun by breakers on a southern shore.
"This way is best, before we both get hurt."
Look how I turn there, featureless, inert.
That weary phrase moves me to stroke her hand
While winds play with the corners of her skirt.

Better to lie, to swear some decent pledge,
To resurrect the buried heart again;
To twirl a glass and smile, as in pain,
At a small table by the water's edge.
"Yes, this is best, things might have grown much worse. . ."

And that is all the truth, it could be worse;
All is exhilaration on the eve,
Especially, when the self-seeking heart
So desperate for some mirror to believe
Finds in strange eyes the old original curse.
So cha cha cha, begin the long goodbyes,
Leave the half-tasted sorrows of each pledge,
At a small table by the water's edge.

I walk with her into the brightening street;
Stores rattling shut, as brief dusk fills the city.
Only the gulls, hunting the water's edge
Wheel like our lives, seeking something worth pity.

RUINS OF A GREAT HOUSE

Though our longest sun sets at right
declensions and makes but winter
arches, it cannot be long before we
lie down in darkness, and have our
light in ashes. . . .

Browne : *Urn Burial*

Stones only, the disjecta membra *of this Great House,*
Whose moth-like girls are mixed with candledust,
Remain to file the lizard's dragonish claws;
The moths of those gate cherubs streaked with stain
Of cattle droppings.

                          Three crows flap for the trees,
And settle, creaking the eucalyptus boughs.
A smell of dead limes quickens in the nose
The leprosy of Empire.

                         "Farewell, green fields"
                         "Farewell, ye happy groves!"

Marble as Greece, like Faulkner's south in stone,
Deciduous beauty prospered and is gone;
A spade below dead leaves will ring the bone
Of some dead animal or human thing
Fallen from evil days, from evil times.

It seems that the original crops were limes
Grown in the silt that clogs the river's skirt;
The imperious rakes are gone, their bright girls gone,
The river flows, obliterating hurt.
I climbed a wall with the grill ironwork
Of exiled craftsmen, protecting that great house
From guilt, perhaps, but not from the worm's rent,
Nor from the padded cavalry of the mouse.
And when a wind shook in the limes I heard

What Kipling heard; the death of a great empire, the abuse
Of ignorance by Bible and by sword.

A green lawn, broken by low walls of stone
Dipped to the rivulet, and pacing, I thought next
Of men like Hawkins, Walter Raleigh, Drake,
Ancestral murderers and poets, more perplexed
In memory now by every ulcerous crime.
The world's green age then was a rotting lime
Whose stench became the charnel galleon's text.
The rot remains with us, the men are gone.
But, as dead ash is lifted in a wind,
That fans the blackening ember of the mind,
My eyes burned from the ashen prose of Donne.

Ablaze with rage, I thought
Some slave is rotting in this manorial lake,
And still the coal of my compassion fought:
That Albion too, was once
A colony like ours, "Part of the continent, piece of the main"
Nook-shotten, rook o'er blown, deranged
By foaming channels, and the vain expense
Of bitter faction.

               All in compassion ends
So differently from what the heart arranged:
"as well as if a manor of thy friend's . . ."

TRAVELOGUE

Sparse colonies of complexions and hills of seasonless
Handsomeness are here; also civilized gestures
In feverless towns of this archipelago.

Filial as shrubs under broad North America,
Or saucier as offshoots of the South Continent
Live these untroubled healers of winter, these worlds

We dreamed of in travelogues and gorgeous poster;
And when the brassy visitor from the hard cities
In coloured shirts, sees our soft actual harbours,

O warn him, Terror, of contagions he knows well,
That we who seem unreal are only willing
To accept the glamour as a fierce background to sorrow

Samuel Selvon

Samuel Selvon was born in Trinidad and is a novelist who has written with humour and sympathy of the poor people of Trinidad, both in his own island and in England. *A Brighter Sun* (1952), *The Lonely Londoners* (1956) and *Turn again Tiger* (1958) are his best-known works. He recently published a successful anthology of West Indian short stories.

CALYPSONIAN

It had a time when things were really brown in Trinidad, and Razor Blade couldn't make a note nohow, no matter what he do, everywhere he turn, people telling him they ain't have work. It look like if work scarce like gold, and is six months now he ain't working.

Besides that, Razor Blade owe Chin parlour about five dollars, and the last time he went in for a sandwich and a sweet drink, Chin tell him no more trusting until he pay all he owe. Chin have his name in a copybook under the counter.

"Wait until the calypso season start," he tell Chin, "and I go be reaping a harvest. You remember last year how much money I had?"

But though Chin remember last year, that still ain't make him soften up, and it reach a position where he hungry, clothes dirty, and he see nothing at all to come, and this time so, the calypso season about three four months off.

On top of all that, rain falling nearly every day, and the shoes he have on have big hole in them, like if they laughing.

Was the rain what cause him to t'ief a pair of shoes from by a shoemaker shop in Park Street. Is the first time he ever t'ief, and it take him a long time to make up his mind. He stand up there on the pavement by this shoemaker shop, and he thinking things like Oh God when I tell you I hungry, and all the shoes around the table, on the ground, some capsize, some old and some new, some getting half sole and some getting new heel.

It have a pair just like the one he have on.

The table cut up for so, as if the shoemaker blind and cutting the wood instead of the leather, and it have a broken calabash shell with some boil starch in it. The starch look like pap; he so hungry he feel he could eat it.

Well, the shoemaker in the back of the shop, and it only have few people sheltering rain on the pavement. It look so easy for him to put down the old pair and take up another pair—this time so, he done have his eye fix on a pair that look like Technic, and just his size, too, besides.

Razor Blade remembered how last year he was sitting pretty— two-tone Technic, gaberdeen suit, hot tie. Now that he catching his royal, every time he only make comparison with last year, thinking in his mind how them was the good old days, and wondering if they go ever come back again.

And it look to him as if t'iefing could be easy, because plenty time people does leave things alone and go away, like how now the shoemaker in the back of the shop, and all he have to do is take up a pair of shoes and walk off in cool blood.

Well, it don't take plenty to make a t'ief. All you have to do is have a fellar catching his royal, and can't get a work noway, and bam! By the time he make two three rounds he bounce something somewhere, an orange from a tray, or he snatch a bread in a parlour, or something.

Like how he bounce the shoes.

So though he frighten like hell and part of him going like a pliers, Razor Blade playing victor brave boy and whistling as he go down the road.

The only thing now is that he hungry.

Right there by Queen Street, in front of a Chinee restaurant, he get an idea. Not an idea in truth; all he did think was: In for a shilling in for a pound. But when he think that, is as if he begin to realize that if he going to get stick for the shoes, he might as well start t'iefing black is white.

So he open now to anything: all you need is a start, all you need is a crank up, and it come easy after that.

What you think he planning to do? He planning to walk in the Chinee restaurant and sit down and eat a major meal, and then out off without paying. It look so easy, he wonder why he never think of it before.

The waitress come up while he looking at the menu. She stand up there, with a pencil stick up on she ears like a real test, and when he take a pint at she he realize that this restaurant work only part-time as far as she concern, because she look as if she sleepy, she body bend up like a piece of copper wire.

What you go do? She must be only getting a few dollars from the Chinee man, and she can't live on that.

He realize suddenly that he bothering about the woman when he himself catching his tail, so he shake his head and watch down at the menu.

He mad to order a portion of everything—fry rice, chicken chop-suey, roast pork, chicken chow-min, birdnest soup, chicken broth and one of them big salad with big slice of tomato and onion.

He begin to think again about the last calypso season, when he was holding big, and uses to go up by the high-class Chinee restaurant in St. Vincent Street. He think how is a funny thing how sometimes you does have so much food that you eat till you sick, and another time you can't even see you way to hustle a rock and mauby.

It should have some way that when you have the change you could eat enough to last you for a week or a month, and he make a plan right there, that the next time he have money (Oh God) he go make a big deposit in a restaurant, so that all he have to do is walk in and eat like stupidness.

But the woman getting impatient. She say: "You taking a long time to make up you mind, like you never eat in restaurant before."

And he think about the time when he had money, how no frowsy woman could have talk to him so. He remember how them waitresses used to hustle to serve him, and one night the talk get around that Razor Blade, the Calypsonian, was in the place, and they insist that he give them a number. Which one it was again? The one about Home and the Bachelor.

"Come, come, make up you mind, mister, I have work to do."

So he order plain boil rice and chicken stew, because the way he feeling, all them fancy Chinee dish is only joke, he feel as if he want something like roast breadfruit and saltfish, something solid so when it go down in you belly you could feel it there.

And he tell the woman to bring a drink of Barbados rum first thing, because he know how long they does take to bring food in them restaurant, and he could coast with the rum in the meantime.

By the time the food come he feeling so hungry he could hardly wait, he fall down on the plate of rice and chicken as if is the first time he see food, and in three minute everything finish.

And is just as if he seeing the world for the first time, he feel like a million, he feel like a lord; he give a loud belch and bring up some of the chicken and rice to his throat; when he swallow it back down it taste sour.

He thinking how it had a time an American fellar hear a calypso in Trinidad and he went back to the States and he get it set up to music and thing, and he get the Andrews Sisters to sing it, and the song make money like hell, it was on Hit Parade and all; wherever you turn, you could hear people singing that calypso. This time so, the poor calypsonian who really write the song catching hell in Trinidad; it was only when some smart lawyer friend tell him about copyright and that sort of business that he wake up. He went to America; and how you don't know he get a lot of money after the case did fix up in New York!

Razor Blade know the story good; whenever he write a calypso, he always praying that some big-shot from America would hear it and like it, and want to set it up good. The Blade uses to go in Frederick Street and Marine Square by the one-two music shops, and look at all the popular songs, set up in notes and words, with the name of the fellar who write it big on the front, and sometimes his photograph too. And Razor Blade uses to think: "But why I can't write song like that too, and have my name all over the place?"

And when things was good with him, he went inside now and then, and tell the clerks and them that he does write calypsos. But they only laugh at him, because they does think that calypso is no song at all, that what is song is numbers like 'I've Got You Under

My Skin' and 'Sentimental Journey', what real American composers write.

And the Blade uses to argue that every dog has his day, and that a time would come when people singing calypso all over the world like stupidness.

He thinking about all that as he lean back there in the Chineeman restaurant.

Is to peel off now without paying!

The best way is to play brassface, do as if you own the damn restaurant, and walk out cool.

So he get up and he notice the waitress not around (she must be serving somebody else) and he take time and walk out, passing by the cashier who writing something in a book.

But all this time, no matter how boldface you try to be, you can't stop part of you from going like a pliers, clip, clip, and he feel as if he want to draw his legs together and walk with two foot as one.

When the waitress find out Razor Blade gone without paying, she start to make one set of noise, and a Chinee man from the kitchen dash outside to see if he could see him, but this time so Razor Blade making races down Frederick Street.

The owner of the restaurant tell the woman she have to pay for the food that Razor Blade eat, that was she fault, and she begin to cry big water, because is a lot of food that Razor Blade put away, and she know that that mean two three dollars from she salary.

This time so, Razor Blade laughing like hell; he quite down by the Railway Station, and he know nobody could catch him now.

One set of rain started to fall suddenly; Razor Blade walking like a king in his new shoes, and no water getting up his foot this time, so he ain't even bothering to shelter.

And he don't know why, but same time he get a sharp idea for a calypso. About how a man does catch his royal when he can't get a work noway. The calypso would say about how he see some real hard days; he start to think up words right away as he walking in the rain:

> It had a time in this colony
> When everybody have money excepting me

76

I can't get a work no matter how I try
It look as if good times pass me by.

He start to hum it to the tune of an old calypso ('Man Centipede Bad Too Bad') just to see how it shaping up.

And he think about One Foot Harper, the one man who could help him out with a tune.

It had a big joke with One Foot one time. Somebody t'ief One Foot crutch one day when he was catching a sleep under a weeping willow tree in Woodford Square, and One Foot had to stay in the square for a whole day and night. You could imagine how he curse stink; everybody only standing up and laughing like hell; nobody won't lend a hand, and if wasn't for Razor Blade, now so One Foot might still be waiting under the weeping willow tree for somebody to get a crutch for him.

But the old Blade help out the situation, and since that time, the both of them good friends.

So Razor Blade start making a tack for the tailor shop which part One Foot does always be hanging out, because One Foot ain't working noway, and every day he there by the tailor shop, sitting down on a soapbox and talking whole day.

But don't fret you head, One Foot ain't no fool; it had a time in the old days when they uses to call him King of Calypso, and he was really good. If he did have money, or education business, is a sure thing he would have been up the ladder, because he was the first man who ever had the idea that calypsonians should go away and sing in America and England. But people only laugh at One Foot when he say that.

Razor Blade met One Foot in a big old talk about the time when the Town Hall burn down (One Foot saying he know the fellar who start the fire). When One Foot see him, he stop arguing right away and he say:

"What happening paleets, long time no see."

Razor Blade say: "Look man, I have a sharp idea for a calypso. Let we go in the back of the shop and work it out."

But One Foot feeling comfortable on the soapbox. He say: "Take ease, don't rush me. What about the shilling you have for me, that you borrow last week?"

The Blade turn his pockets inside out, and a pair of dice roll out, and a penknife fall on the ground.

"Boy, I ain't have a cent. I broken. I bawling. If you stick me with a pin you won't draw blood."

"Don't worry with that kind of talk, is so with all-you fellars you does borrow a man money and then forget his address."

"I telling you, man," Razor Blade talk as if he in a hurry, but is only to get away from the topic, "you don't believe me?"

But the Foot cagey. He say, "All right, all right, but I telling you in front that if you want money borrow again, you come to the wrong man. I ain't lending you a nail till you pay me back that shilling that you have for me." The Foot moved off the soap-box, and stand up balancing on the crutch.

"Come, man, do quick," Razor Blade make as if to go behind the shop in the backroom. Same time he see Rahamut, the Indian tailor.

"What happening, Indian, things looking good with you."

Rahamut stop stitching a khaki pants and look at the Blade.

"You and One Foot always writing calypso in this shop, all-you will have to give me a commission."

"Well, you know how it is, sometimes you up, sometimes you down. Right now I so down that bottom and I same thing."

"Well, old man, is a funny thing but I never see you when you up."

"Ah, but wait till the calypso season start."

"Then you won't come round here at all. Then you is bigshot, you forget small fry like Rahamut."

Well, Razor Blade don't know what again to tell Rahamut, because is really true all what the Indian saying about he and One Foot hanging out behind the shop. And he thing about these days when anybody tell him anything, all you could say is: "Wait till the calypso season start up," as if when the calypso season start up God go come to earth, and make everybody happy.

So what he do is he laugh kiff-kiff and give Rahamut a pat on the back, like they is good friends.

Same time One Foot come up, so they went and sit down by a break-up table.

Razor Blade say: "Listen to these words, old man, you never

hear calypso like this in you born days," and he start to give the Foot the words.

But from the time he start, One Foot chock his fingers in his ears and bawl out: "Oh God, old man, you can't think up something new, is the same old words every year."

"But how you mean, man," the Blade say, "this is calypso, father. Wait until you hear the whole thing."

They begin to work on the song, and One Foot so good that in two twos he fix up a tune. So Razor Blade pick up a empty bottle and a piece of stick, and One Foot start beating the table, and is so they getting on, singing this new calypso that they invent.

Well, Rahamut and other Indian fellar who does help him out with the sewing come up and listen.

"What you think of this new number, papa?" the Blade ask Rahamut.

Rahamut scratch his head and say: "Let me get that tune again."

So they begin again, beating on the table and the bottle, and Razor Blade imagine that he singing to a big audience in the Calypso Tent, so he putting all he have in it.

When they finished the fellar who does help Rahamut say: "That is hearts."

But Rahamut say: "Why you don't shut your mouth? What all-you Indian know about calypso?"

And that cause a big laugh, everybody begin to laugh kya-kya, because Rahamut himself is an Indian.

One Foot turn to Razor Blade and say: "Listen to them two Indian how they arguing about we creole calypso. I never see that in my born days!"

Rahamut say: "Man, I is a creolise Trinidadian, *oui*."

Razor Blade say: "All right, joke is joke, but all-you think it good? It really good?"

Rahamut want to say yes, it good, but he beating about the bush, he hemming and hawing, he saying: "Well, it so-so," and "It not so bad," and "I hear a lot of worse ones."

But the fellar who does help Rahamut, he getting on as if he mad, he only hitting Razor Blade and One Foot on the shoulder and saying how he never hear calypso like that, how it sure to be the

Road March for the next year Carnival. He swinging his hands all about in the air while he talking, and his hand hit Rahamut hand and Rahamut get a chook in his finger with a needle he was holding.

Well, Rahamut put the finger in his mouth and start to suck it, and he turn round and start to abuse the other tailor fellar, saying why don't you keep you tail quiet, look you make me chook my hand with the blasted needle?

"Well, what happen for that? You go dead because a needle chook you?" the fellar say.

Big argument start up; they forget all about Razor Blade calypso and start to talk about how people does get blood poison from pin and needle chook.

Well, it don't have anything to write down as far as the calypso concern. Razor Blade memorize the words and tune, and that is the case. Is so a calypso born, cool cool, without any fuss. Is so all them big numbers like 'Yes, I Catch Him Last Night', and 'That Is a Thing I Can Do Anytime Anywhere' and 'Old Lady Your Bloomers Falling Down', born right there behind Rahamut tailor shop.

After the big talk about pin and needle Rahamut and the fellar who does assist him went back to finish off a zootsuit that a fellar was going to call for in the evening.

Now Razor Blade want to ask One Foot to borrow him a shilling, but he don't know how to start, especially as he owe him already. So he begin to talk sweet, praising up the tune that One Foot invent for the calypso, saying he never hear a tune so sweet, that the melody smooth like sweet-oil.

But as soon as he start to come like that, the old Foot begin to get cagey, and say: "Oh God, old man, don't mamaguile me."

The Blade not so very fussy, because a solid meal in his belly. But same time he trying to guile One Foot into lending him a little thing, he get an idea.

He begin to tell One Foot how he spend the morning, how he ups and takes the shoes from the shoemaker shop in Park Street, and how he eat big for nothing.

One Foot say: "I bet you get in trouble, all-you fellars does take some brave risk, *oui*."

Razor say: "Man, it easy as kissing hand, is only because you have one foot and can't run fast, that's why you talking so."

Foot say: "No jokes about my one foot."

Razor say: "But listen, man, you too stupid again! You and me could work up a good scheme to get some money. If you t'iefing, you might as well t'ief big."

"Is you is the t'ief, not me."

"But listen, man, Foot," the Blade gone down low in voice, "I go do everything, all I want you to do is to keep watchman for me, to see if anybody coming."

"What is the scheme you have?"

To tell truth, the old Blade ain't have nothing cut and dry in the old brain; all he thinking is that he go make a big t'ief somewhere where have money. He scratch his head and pull his ears like he did see Spencer Tracy do in a picture, and he say: "What about the Roxy Theatre down St. James?"

Same time he talking, he feeling excitement in his body, like if waves going up and coming down and he hold on to One Foot hand.

The Foot say: "Well, yes, the day reach when you really catching you royal. I never thought I would see the time when my good friend Razor Blade turn t'ief. Man, you sure to get catch. Why you don't try for a work somewhere until the calypso season start up?"

"I tired try to get work. It ain't have work noway."

"Well, you ain't no t'ief. You sure to get catch, I tell you."

"But, man, look how I get away with the shoes and the meal! I tell you all you have to do is play boldface and you could commit murder and get away free."

The Foot start to hum an old calypso:

> If a man have money today . . .
> He could commit murder and get away free
> And live in the Governor's company . . .

The Blade begin to get vex. "So you don't like the idea? You think I can't get away with it?"

"You ain't have no practice. You is a novice. Crime does not pay."

"You is a damn coward!"

"Us calypsonians have to keep we dignity."

"You go to hell! If you won't help me I go do it by myself, you go see! And I not t'iefing small, I t'iefing big! If I going down the river, I making sure is for plenty money, and not for no small-time job."

"Well, papa, don't say I ain't tell you you looking for trouble."

"Man Foot, the trouble with you is you only have one foot so you can't think like me."

The Foot get hot. He say: "Listen, I tell you already no jokes about my one foot, you hear? I ain't taking no jokes about that. Curse my mother, curse my father, but don't tell me nothing about my foot."

The Blade relent. "I sorry, Foot, I know you don't like nobody to give you jokes."

Same time Rahamut call out and ask why they keeping so much noise, if they think they in the fishmarket.

So they finish the talk, Razor Blade tell One Foot he would see him later, and One Foot say: "Righto, boy, don't forget the words for the song. And I warning you for the last time to keep out of trouble."

But the minute he leave the tailor shop Razor Blade only thinking how easy it go to be to pull off this big deal. He alone would do it, without any gun, too, besides.

Imagine the Foot saying he is a novice! All you need is brass-face; play brazen; do as if you is a saint, as if you still have you mother innocent features, and if anybody ask you anything, lift up you eyebrows and throw you hands up in the air and say: "Oh Lord, who, *me?*"

He find himself quite round by the Queen's Park Savannah, walking and thinking. And he see a old woman selling oranges. The woman as if she sleeping in the heat, she propping up she chin with one hand, and she head bend down. Few people passing; Razor Blade size up the situation in one glance.

He mad to bounce a orange from the tray, just to show that he could do it and get away. Just pass up near—don't even look down at the tray—and just lift one up easy as you walking, and put it in you pocket.

He wish One Foot was there to see how easy it was to do.

But he hardly put the orange in his pocket when the old woman jump up and start to make one set of noise, bawling out: "T'ief, t'ief! Look a man t'ief a orange from me! Help! Hold him! Don't let 'im get away!"

And is as if that bawling start the pliers working on him right away; he forget everything he was thinking, and he start to make races across the savannah.

He look back and see three fellars chasing him. And is just as if he can't feel nothing at all, as if he not running, as if he standing up in one spot. The only thing is the pliers going clip clip, and he gasping: "Oh God! Oh God!"

Mervyn Morris

Born in Kingston in 1937, Mervyn Morris is considered in Jamaica as the most outstanding of the younger poets. Most of his work has been published in West Indian magazines such as *Bim*, *Caribbean Quarterly* and *Public Opinion*. He himself states that he is fond of particular poems rather than of particular poets, but that his favourite poets are perhaps Shakespeare and R. S. Thomas. In reading Mervyn Morris it is difficult not to be reminded of the English metaphysical poets, since one of his distinguishing features is the quality of thought emotion. He is often ironical and certainly unromantic. He feels that poetry should be fairly accessible and communicable, and yet improve on re-readings.

THE DAY MY FATHER DIED

The day my father died
I could not cry;
My mother cried,
Not I.

His face on the pillow
In the dim light
Wrote mourning to me,
Black and white.

We saw him struggle,
Stiffen, relax;
The face fell empty,
Dead as wax.

I'd read of death
But never seen.
My father's face, I swear,
Was not serene.

84

Topple that lie
However appealing;
That face was absence
Of all feeling.

My mother's tears were my tears,
Each sob shook me:
The pain of death is living,
The dead are free.

For me my father's death
Was not her sorrow;
That day was her day,
Loss was tomorrow.

BIRTHDAY HONOURS

Your birthday; so I sit
Cudgelling the brain for tunes to whistle,
Pondering love and anniversaries.

So many perfect poems have lied
Of love sublime or love decaying or dead.
Though your man Donne, thinking his way to truth,
Moulds spirit and senses into sinewy lines
Wriggling their honesty to life,
Yet even he must lie, forcing a form
Where no form is, tidying
Where order is untrue.
Love is a theme for prose.

Your fullest year has withered in a night.
"The page is turned" or "Time has dug a tomb,
The months and minutes buried in its depths,
Silent beyond recall."
"What fools we are who must fragment
The long continuous string of time!

Birthdays are only knots, the small reminders
That time will stop, that human beauty fades."
"Birthdays are the firm consoling corners
In the long dark echoing room of time."

Time is a lie, the past is now
And all our futures are our present minutes;
There is no string of time, neatly unravelling
Its agelong progress till the end is cut,
Only a dark pool swirling with living moments,
Love-letters, matches, galliwasps,
Empty old toothpaste-tubes and railway tickets,
Markers that flow from my time into yours,
Ours into others', others' into ours,
For all our times are one, the pool's confusion
Is falsified by cuckoo-clocks and calendars.

Thus wildly I celebrate my birthday singing yours,
Loving, I swear that love in art is lies,
And, wanting art, must swear that art is falsehood,
And in the whirlpool, clutching at straws,
Must pray through love and art
That something I can do may outlive time.

TO A WEST INDIAN DEFINER

Your intellect feels discontent
With having and not labelling.
Three million people
And our several territories,
Africa England America Portugal and Spain
India and France China Syria
Black brown yellow pink and cream
Young middle-aged decrepit vital,
John-Cunnu Kelee Carnival
Hosein La-Marguerite and Independence-Day
Our English hymns creole proverbs

Steel band calypso rock-'n'-roll
Anancy-stories obeah and Christ,
The village bram and Yacht Regattas
Poverty clay-pigeon-shooting
Slavery bastards laughter riots
My uncle's waistcoat and his gardener's sweat,
Labba creek-water flying-fish
Bush-tea hot-dogs and coca-cola
Black-pudding roti cuckoo dalpourri,
Drought and hurricane, mountain soil and sea—
All these
All these and more you wish
To fix in one quick-drying definition.
You must not try to cram us all
Into your little box;
Your definition must perforce be false
Or we are dead.

George Lamming

George Lamming, who was born in Barbados in 1927, is essentially a novelist, and has written a number of semi-autobiographical novels such as: *In the Castle of my Skin* (1953), *The Emigrants* (1954), *The Pleasures of Exile* (1960). He now lives in London and is a frequent broadcaster for the B.B.C.

BIRTHDAY WEATHER

Rain, rain, rain . . . and they flattered me with the consolation that my birthday had brought showers of blessing. The morning laden with cloud and uncertain of the sun soon passed into noon, and the noon neutral and silent into the sodden grimness of an evening that waded through water. That evening I kept an eye on the crevices of our wasted roof where the colour of the shingles had turned to mourning black, and waited for the weather to rehearse my wishes. But the evening settled on the slush of the roads that dissolved in parts into pools of clay, and I wept for the watery waste of my ninth important day. Yet I was wrong, my mother protested: it was irreverent to disapprove the will of the Lord or reject the consolation that my birthday had brought showers of blessing.

It was my ninth celebration of the gift of life, my ninth celebration. From a window where the spray had given the sill a little wet life I watched the water ride through the lanes and alleys that multiplied behind the barracks that neighboured our house. The white stalks of the lily no longer resisted the force of the hammering rain, but coaxed their roots from the earth and drifted across the upturned clay, into the canals and on to the deep black river where by agreement the floods converged. The water rose higher and higher until the fern and flowers that favoured our veranda were flooded. Through the flaws of the door it entered, and expanded across the uncarpeted borders of the floor. My mother brought sacks that absorbed it quickly but overhead the crevices of the

88

roof were weeping rain, and surfacing the carpet and the epergne of flowers and fern were liquid and glittering curves which the mourning black of the shingles had bequeathed. No one seemed to notice how the noon had passed into evening, the evening to night; nor to worry that the weather had played me false. Nothing mattered but the showers of blessing and the eternal will of the water's source. And I might have accepted the consolation forthwith if it weren't that the floods had chosen to follow me in the celebration of all my years, evoking the image of those legendary waters which had once arisen to set a curse on the course of man.

As if in serious imitation of the waters that raced outside, our lives, meaning our fears and their corresponding ideals, seemed to escape down an imaginary drain that was our future. Our capacity for feeling had grown as large as the flood, but every trick of communication, words, gestures and tears, seemed as precariously adequate as the house hoisted on water. Of course it was difficult to see what was happening outside, but there were paddling plashes of boys' feet and the choke of an engine stuck in mud.

The village was a marvel of small, heaped houses raised jauntily on groundsels of limestone, and arranged in rows on either side of the multiplying marl roads. Sometimes the roads disintegrated, the limestone slid back and the houses advanced across their boundaries to meet those on the opposite side in an embrace of board and shingle and cactus fence. The white marl roads made four at each crossing, except where the road narrowed to a lane or alley that led into a tenant's backyard. There were shops at each crossing: one, two, sometimes three, and so positioned that the respective owners could gauge each others' fortunes. And wherever there was a shop there was a street lamp ringed to a post, and always much activity, and often the naked stench of raw living. The lamps were fuelled with gas and lit at six every evening. When the lights went on, little boys like a bevy of flies harbouring dung assembled around the lamp-post for gossip and stories. Elsewhere in a similar manner men gathered to throw dice or cut cards. The spectacle repeated itself at each crossing where there was a street lamp ringed to a post. The roads bore names: Murrell, Alkins, Hunt, and a curious one-way affection grew between the villager and the road he lived in; just as a mutual antipathy sometimes passed from dwellers in one road to those in another. Now and again the dwellers at Alkins would contrive a secret conspiracy against those at Murrell, and the verdict was always the same. The people in Hunt's road, those in Alkins would declare, were a lot of so-and-so's. There was a public bath for men and women with a perpetual stench of E.C. pervading the air, and everywhere limestone constructions like roofless ovens for the disposal of garbage. But most notable was the wood of mahogany and fustic trees through which the trains passed from the city on their excursions to the country. There were days when the village was quiet; the shoemaker plied lazily at his trade and the washerwomen bent over the tubs droned away their complacency. At other times there were scenes of terror, and more than once there was a scene of murder.

But the season of flood could change everything. The floods could level the stature and even conceal the identity of the village. With the turn of my ninth year it happened again. From the window I looked at the uniform wreckage of a village at night in water. My mother said it was a shame, as was everything that displeased her. And even after many years I would try to fix her label. What precisely was a shame? Was it the weather of the village or the human condition in which and in spite of which the poor had sworn their loyalty to life? But so she said; and having said that, she would suspend her judgement and in an attitude of prayer reminded me of blessings that might have missed my memory.

So I went away from the window over the dripping sacks and into a corner which the weather had forgotten. And what did I remember? My father who had only fathered the idea of me had left me the sole liability of my mother who really fathered me. And beyond that my memory was a blank. It sank with its cargo of episodes like a crew that prefer scuttle to the consequences of survival. Moreover, my mother began to sing, which always happened when I tried to remember. Her voice was clear and colourless. It could indicate but not control a tune which I recognized only through the words.

"I can't get it right, tonight," she said.

No answer.

"You know, George, we haven't had rain like this for a long, long time."

No answer.

"You listening?"

"Yes."

Then she broke into a soft repetitive tone which rose with every fresh surge of feeling until it became a scattering peal of solicitude that soared across the night and into the neighbour's house. And the answer came back louder, better organized and more communicative, so that another neighbour responded and yet another until the voices seemed to be gathered up by a single effort and the whole village shook with a song on its foundation of water. My mother was pleased with her unacclaimed but generally accepted supervision. She lit the big brass lamp that hung from a beam bridging the slopes of the ceiling. The space of the ceiling which was directly over the lamp wore a surface of polished brass. The flames spluttered along the blue burnt edge of the wick. Standing beneath the flowered brass bowl that contained the fuel, my mother regulated the pitch of the blaze. The smoke circled the flames within the chimney and later settled on the wet ceiling. The light pushed its way about the corners of the house. The partitions in their dying response looked a dismal wreck in reflection. It was the uncertain light one feels on the passage from sleep to conscious waking. The clock shelved in one corner kept up its ticking, each second falling with uncanny effect on the corresponding leap of the heart. My mother retreated to another part of the house where the silk and taffeta designs of her needling were being revised and reversed. I soon followed like a lean trail of smoke tracing a radius round its red origin. And for memory I had substituted enquiry.

"Where you say my grandmother went?"

"To Panama," my mother answered. "It was the opening of the canal. She is now in Canal Zone. It's time you learn to write her a letter."

"And my grandfather who was your father?" I went on.

"Oh, he died, my chil', he died before I was born."

"And my uncle who was your brother?"

"My brother went to America," my mother said. "It's years now. The last we heard he was on a boat and then take sick, and is probably dead for all we know." Her feelings were neutral.

"And when my uncle who was your brother, and my grandmother who was your mother, when they went away how old you wus?"

"Two."

"Two years?"

"Yes. Two," my mother said.

My birth began with an absence of family relations. My parents on almost all sides had been deposited in the bad or uncertain accounts of all my future relationships, and loneliness from which had subsequently grown the terrible consolation of freedom was the legacy with which my first year opened.

My mother seated beside me and in front of the sewing machine must have sensed the change progressing within me. Memory was again pursuing the line of discovery which enquiry had left off. Late as it was, my birthday was still alive. The morning had opened in clouds which had dissolved the noon into a wet and sudden night. I had had tea and a bun in the backhouse, and the promise of a cake with nine candles. But the candles had been blown out before the cake arrived, and the showers blessing the day had presumably dissolved the promise like the noon. I wore a long face and a murderous scowl.

"But you can't ask me to make bread out of stone," my mother said. On recollection I admitted there wasn't even stone. And I had to, after what the neighbour had said. It was then noon.

"All you hear what happen to Foster? Why the house wash away, clean, clean, clean, groundsel, everything gone clean. They put Miss Foster and the children in the Guard House, and you know how many children Miss Foster got?"

"And Mr. Foster?" my mother enquired.

"I was coming to that. Foster swear he won't leave the old house, and went sailing down the river on the roof. They had to fish him from the Deanery wall with a rope."

The neighbour closed her window and stuffed the crevices with brown paper.

Since it made no difference whether it was noon or night I went to the backhouse to play with my pigeon. It was asleep on the rod that served every condition of the bird's accommodation. I took it down and patted the head and neck. Its claws ringed the index finger of my left hand as I fought to open the beak with the other. Then I fed it till the craw expanded to a pleated curve of feather flesh, and the shoulders drooped and the eyes closed over a film of water. And immediately I emptied a phial of castor oil down the throat, remembering the villagers always said there was nothing better than to eat well and purge clean. I returned the pigeon to the rod and looked round through the gaping roof at the sky which could not be distinguished between night and noon. That night the pigeon died and I with a burning shame in my head buried my blessings in the pillow. My mother lay beside me re-counting the incidents of the previous day and rehearsing rough-and-ready plans for the next. In the dark the crevices of the roof were concealed, but occasional raindrops fell against the bedposts in a scatter of specks that dissolved on my nose. I opened my eyes and saw enormous phantoms with eyes of fire and crowned with bull's horns stalking through the dark. I closed my eyes and the phantoms went. I opened them again, and one came forward hovering over my head in a jeering silence. I struck a blow that sliced the unfeeling figure of the demon, and my knuckles crashed against the bedposts. My mother groaned.

"The kitchen in a state," she said, "and maybe rainwater get into the barrel."

The barrel was the iron drum in which we kept our drinking water. Once a week a sanitary inspector poked his nose into it and scraped the side with his long enamel spoon in search of larvae.

"Take yer head out of my water," my mother once snapped. "You can put it in the W.C. if you like, but not my water."

The inspector was offended and made a note in his little blue book.

"Good day," he said, and fled.

I laughed as I recalled the incident. It was an odd little giggle that leapt in my throat, and my mother groaned again.

"The kitchen in a state," she repeated. "And the last time you had rainwater you got belly ache. And the inspector coming to-morrow."

My mother sometimes talked mechanically.

My eyes opened and the phantoms were still there. I crossed the pillows across my head and clutched the stitched edges of the sheet to my ears.

And my birthday drifted outside in a fog of blackness that covered the land. The lanes and alleys crossed and multiplied below the tides that towed limestone and clay, shingle and brick through the canals and pipes and to the river that ran far and wide into the sea. At the street corners the gas lamps may have winked within their netted cages, and the light leaking past the frosty domes may have fallen dully on the water. The moon may have stuck somewhere beyond the cluster of mahogany, remote and ineffectual. But the hardy poor like their stalled beloved in the distant cemetery slept peacefully beneath the flying spray. All the voices were hushed, the puddles deserted, the gurgle of the wrestling flood submerged. My birthday making its black departure from the land had been blessed with showers whose consolation was my blessing.

Claude McKay

Born in Jamaica in 1890, Claude McKay was the first Caribbean poet and novelist writing in English to gain an international reputation. He left Jamaica in 1912 and spent the rest of his life in the United States and Europe. He died in 1948.

While in the United States he identified himself with the sufferings of the American Negroes, and many of his poems at this period reflect the sorrow, bitterness and, at times, the anger he felt when confronted with racial discrimination and persecution. *If We Must Die* and *Lynching* belong to this phase of his writing. When he wrote about Jamaica, his poetry became nostalgic and lyrical, for he was not only remembering his native land but also his vanished childhood and youth. McKay is spontaneous and direct, sometimes trite in his poetic idiom. As he writes in his introduction to *Harlem Shadows* (1922): "I have not hesitated to use words which are old, and in some poetic circles considered poetically over-worked, when I thought I could make them glow alive by new manipulation." But it is the force of his emotion and his sincerity which override his sometimes hackneyed expression and make his poetry live.

FLAME-HEART

So much have I forgot in ten years,
So much in ten brief years. I have forgot
What time the purple apples come to juice,
And what month brings the shy forget-me-not.
I have forgot the special startling season
Of the pimento's flowering and fruiting;
What time of year the ground doves brown the fields
And fill the noonday with their curious fluting.
I have forgotten much, but still remember
The poinsettia's red, blood-red, in warm December.

I still recall the honey-fever grass,
But cannot recollect the high days when
We rooted them out of the ping-wing path
To stop the mad bees in the rabbit pen.

95

I often try to think in what sweet month
The languid painted ladies used to dapple
The yellow by-road mazing from the main,
Sweet with the golden threads of the rose-apple.
I have forgotten—but strange—but quite remember
The poinsettia's red, blood-red, in warm December.

NORTH AND SOUTH

O sweet are tropic lands for waking dreams.
    There time and life move lazily along.
There by the banks of blue and silver streams
    Grass-sheltered crickets chirp incessant song;
Gay-coloured lizards loll all through the day,
    Their tongues out-stretched for careless little flies.

And swarthy children in the fields at play,
    Look upward, laughing at the smiling skies.
A breath of idleness is in the air
    That casts a subtle spell upon all things,
And love and mating-time are everywhere,
    And wonder to life's commonplace clings.

The fluttering humming-bird darts through the trees,
    And dips his long beak in the big bell-like flowers.
The leisured buzzard floats upon the breeze,
    Riding a crescent cloud for endless hours.
The sea beats softly on the emerald strands—
    O sweet for quiet dreams are tropic lands.

THE LYNCHING

His Spirit in smoke ascended to the high heaven.
His father, by the cruellest way of pain,
Had bidden him to his bosom once again;
The awful sin remained still unforgiven.

All night a bright and solitary star
(Perchance the one that ever guided him,
Yet gave him up at last to Fate's wild whim)
Hung pitifully o'er the swinging char.
Day dawned, and soon the mixed crowds came to view
The ghastly body swaying in the sun.
The women thronged to look, but never a one
Showed sorrow in their eyes of steely blue.

And little lads, lynchers that were to be,
Danced round the dreadful thing in fiendish glee.

IF WE MUST DIE

If we must die, let it not be like hogs
Hunted and penned in an inglorious spot,
While round us bark the mad and hungry dogs,
Making their mock of our accursed lot.
If we must die, O let us nobly die,
So that our precious blood may not be shed
In vain; then even the monsters we defy
Shall be constrained to honour us though dead.
As kinsmen we must meet the common foe.
Though far outnumbered let us show us brave,
And for their thousand blows deal one death blow.
What though before us lies the open grave?
Like men we'll face the murderous, cowardly pack,
Pressed to the wall, dying, but fighting back.

Aimé Césaire

Aimé Césaire was born in Martinique in 1911, and is possibly the most internationally known of Caribbean writers. He was for many years associated with French surrealism. He coined the word *négritude*, which, with the theory it implies, has been taken up by coloured writers both in America and Africa. Briefly, *négritude* can be said to be the awareness in the Negro in any part of the world of being possessed by a peculiar kind of sensibility, different from that of the white man, but in no way inferior. *Négritude* can also be seen as the rejection of white civilization and the setting up of Negro cultural values.

GREETINGS TO THE THIRD WORLD

Oh my island, half asleep and so restless
on the sea.
And suddenly from the points of danger
history makes the sign I had been waiting for.
I see nations sprouting,
red and green and I greet you.
Banners, throats filled with ancient air,
Mali, Guinea, Ghana.

And I see you, men,
not at all clumsy under this new sun.

Listen,
from my distant island
from my brooding island,
I call out to you—Ho.
And your voices answer me
and what they say means:
the day is bright. And it is true
even through storms and night
the day is bright for you.

98

From here I see Kivu descend towards
Tanganyika by the silver stairway of Ruzuzi
(a big girl at each step
bathing the night with the rustling of her hair).

From here I see, knotted together
Benoue, Logone, Tchad;
bound together Senegal and Niger
from here, I hear the Nyaragongo
roaring.

Hatred.
Empty noise, leavings of the hyena,
under a stiff wind, we were all covered
with bruises.
I have seen the slavers' jaws growing smaller.

I see Africa, multiple and one
vertical in the thunderstorm's change of fortune
with it's swellings and nodules,
slightly apart, but within reach
of the century, like a heart in reserve.

And again I say, Oh mother
  and I raise up my strength
  bowing down my face.
  O my land.

Let me crumble it gently between thumb and fore-finger
Let me rub my chest with it, my arms,
my left arm
and let me caress my right arm with it.

Ho, my earth is good,
   Your voice also is good
   it has the appeasing power of a sunset.

Land forge granary. Land showing the way.
It is here a truth is found, light
eclipsing the cruel old artificial gold.

See,
    Africa is no longer
    in the diamond of misery
    a black heart breaking.

Our Africa is a hand out of a gauntlet,
it is a straight hand, palm outwards
fingers tightly pressed together.

It is a swollen hand
a wounded open hand
held out,
    brown, yellow, white

to all the hands, the wounded hands
of the world.

(Translated from the French by G. R. Coulthard.)

Enrique Serpa

Enrique Serpa was born in Cuba in 1899. This story is typical of much writing in Cuba during the period 1900–60 in its dramatization of the life of under-privileged people such as cane-cutters, fishermen and small farmers, and in its focusing of attention on social injustice. The photographic realism of this story is characteristic of Serpa and many others dealing with similar subjects.

SHARK FINS

Felipe had the strange feeling that the sound of the alarm clock was following like a large fish through the waters of sleep. Still not fully awake, he noticed that his wife was stirring by his side. He opened his eyes and saw a beam of light falling like a golden cactus leaf from the door. Jumping out of bed in his bare feet, he groped for his shirt and trousers on a box by the bed. Then he put on his shoes, which had no laces, and a dirty cap. He took a box of matches from his pocket and lit an oil lamp.

In the room there was a stifling atmosphere, heavy and sour, made up of dampness, acrid sweat and poverty. Felipe turned and let his eyes rest on his wife's body. She was lying face downwards with her head between her crossed arms. She was half covered by a counterpane of artificial silk, faded and full of patches. One of her calves were showing and a fly buzzed around it a moment before settling. By her side, a newly born child was sleeping, its legs drawn up and arms tucked in, in the position it had had in its mother's womb. The other three children were huddled together in a cot in front of which three rickety chairs had been placed so they would not roll out. One of them, after turning over, began an inarticulate song. Felipe, using his big rough hands with incredible gentleness, shook the child slowly and patted its bottom. It gave a long sigh and then was silent.

The tenement was coming to life at the call of the morning. There was the sound of a metal shutter being pushed up. Then in the distance the grinding of a tram. And immediately after that, the roar of a motor and the strident sound of a horn. A man doubled over in a hoarse, tearing cough, ended with a coarse clearing of his throat. Through the closed door filtered the slip-slop of slippers on the floor. A child's voice rang out happily and a man's voice answered. There was a pause, then the child's voice sounded, jubilant with astonishment: "Dad, see how the dog's barking at you."

Felipe took up the basket which contained his fishing tackle—lines, hooks, sinkers, a can for water—and put it under his arm. He gave a last glance at the cot where the children were sleeping and left the room.

Outside the door, he met an old woman, so old, wrinkled and consumed that she seemed only the shadow of a woman. "And how's Ambrosio?" he said.

The woman screwed her face into an expression of anguish: "Bad, bad, my son. Merse went for a doctor at the hospital, but he wouldn't come and said something about not being on duty. And now I'm waiting for him. I think Ambrosio is going to die."

"You can never tell. Maybe he'll see us all buried," said Felipe in an effort to cheer the old woman up.

The circumstantial evocation of death, however, had clouded his thoughts. And suddenly, as he went on his way he realized that he was remembering an incident he had experienced the previous evening. Provoked by one of those acts of injustice that can turn the most quiet tempered man into a murderer, it could have had tragic consequences. It had all started over a question of sharks fins. For some time, Felipe, like the other fishermen of La Punta and Casa Blanca, had avoided catching sharks. A decree from the President of the Republic had given the monopoly to a private company which, although it could not take full advantage of its privileges, was trying to exploit individual fishermen.

Up to that time, many poor families along the coast had depended on shark fishing to make a living. A Chinese on Zanja Street bought shark fins and tails, salted them and sold them in San Francisco, for these articles, along with swallows' nests and sturgeon soup are some of the most highly valued items in Chinese cooking. He paid two dollars for a set of fins, and this was very good business for the fishermen, since they also kept the rest of the fish. Out of its spine they made walking sticks, which looked like ivory; the teeth were sold as good luck charms, and the heads, dried, were sold as souvenirs to American tourists.

And then, unexpectedly, had come that wretched decree, which had put the Chinese out of business. It did not seem too bad at first when the whole matter was largely theoretical. Agents from the Shark Fishing Company arrived and made the fishermen an offer which seemed reasonable enough. They would buy the sharks and pay according to their length. They spoke eloquently and fast, so much so that the fishermen accepted their proposals with joy, even with gratitude. They very soon realized, however, that they had been tricked. Things were not as the agents had described them and for a fish to be worth a dollar, it had to be abnormally long. Also they had to hand over the entire fish with fins and tail. Not even a small piece of skin could be missing.

The fishermen, in the knowledge that they had been swindled, began to protest, asking for an increase in price. But the Company, without troubling to discuss the matter, referred to the presidential decree, and threatened them with prison. After this it began to exercise its rights tyranically. And the Company could count on the help of the Harbour Police which, stimulated by secret bribes, devoted itself more energetically to catching shark fishers than to catching water-front thieves and smugglers. The whole situation was intolerably unjust, especially as the Company made a profit from the entire fish. It sold the fins to Chinese, the bones to a button factory, the skin to the tanneries. An excellent lubricant was extracted from the livers and sold on the market as whale oil. And to make matters worse, the salted young sharks, only a few weeks old, were sold as 'boneless codfish'.

The result of this was that after a while the fishermen stopped catching sharks. And if by accident a shark got on to their lines, they killed it and left it, cut into pieces in the sea, rather than sell it to the Company for thirty or fifty cents.

Felipe had followed the behaviour of the rest. But as he said, "When things have to happen . . ." A few days previously, out at sea, he had not caught anything, not even a barracuda, which unscrupulous restaurant owners, in order to make a few cents, will serve at the risk of poisoning their customers.

And then suddenly a shark had started to swim round his boat. It was a hammer-head, about fifteen feet long, with long broad fins. Instinctively Felipe reached for his harpoon, but he was stopped by the idea that he was not supposed to catch sharks. So he watched the shark, which looked like a dark, flexible tree-trunk. Yes, it was like a tree-trunk, he thought. How much would it be worth? Felipe calculated that any Chinese in Zanja Street would pay at least two dollars for the fins and tail. He felt he should take those two dollars which the sea was offering so generously, to relieve his extreme poverty. Two dollars meant three good meals for his starving children. But then there were the Police and the agents for the Shark Fishing Company to think about.

On the water-front they were always on the look-out for any fisherman bringing in shark fins or tails. And if sometimes they merely confiscated the catch, at others they arrested the fishermen. And after that five dollars fine and they were not even allowed a defence. But two dollars were two dollars, and however hard he worked, it was possible that that day his wife would have nothing to cook. Fishing was always a game of chance and often one's luck did not depend on one's efforts. If only it were possible to make the fish bite! And those fins there, within the reach of his hands. Two dollars.

He made up his mind. Two dollars, for him. What the hell! Quickly, while he was preparing his harpoon, he threw out all the bait he had to keep the fish around. The shark surfaced, showing its stiff dorsal fins, its white under-belly flashing in the sunlight. When it had eaten the bait, it dived slowly, to emerge a few moments later behind the boat.

The harpoon, skilfully cast by Felipe, caught it in the neck and it struggled convulsively, churning up a whirlpool of water with its tail. A few blows with a mallet on the head were enough to quieten it down. Half an hour later its body, without fins or tail, sank, turning on itself to be eaten by its fellows in the depths of the sea.

Behind the mutilated body, like a silent protest, remained a wake of blood.

After tying the fins and the tail with a piece of cord, Felipe rowed towards the coast. He wanted to get ashore as soon as possible, to go early to China Town in search of a buyer. Perhaps with Chan, the owner of the *Canton*, he might strike a bargain. At worst he ought to exchange the fins for food.

And then suddenly fate, dressed in a blue uniform, arrived. Felipe had scarcely tied up his boat when he was startled by a harsh, sarcastic voice: "This time you can't deny it. I've caught you red-handed." And as he turned, his heart in a vice, he saw a policeman, smiling maliciously and pointing with his fore-finger at the fins and tail. After a moment's silence he added:

"I'll take those."

He bent down to pick them up. But he did not get to touch them because Felipe, jumping forward, grabbed them in his right hand.

"They are mine!" he muttered violently.

For a moment the policeman seemed astonished at meeting such behaviour. But he reacted quickly in an attempt to recover his authority:

"Come on, hand them over or I'll take you and the fins along with me."

Felipe looked at him carefully. He was a small man, skinny and ungainly. His precarious physique was in sharp contrast with his hectoring voice and the stance of a fighting-cock he had assumed. Felipe scowled and felt his arm muscles contract. And aware of his own strength and of the elasticity of his body, he said to himself:

"This fellow isn't even half a man."

In the meantime, a group of onlookers had collected around him and the policeman.

"Hand them over or you'll be sorry."

"Give them to him" advised a voice, that of an old copper-faced fisherman. And changing his tone:

"Perhaps he can see a doctor with what he gets for them."

Felipe felt the weight of innumerable eyes fixed on him and he imagined the scornful smiles and ironical comments with which the witnesses of the scene would taunt him afterwards. And apart from this, the feeling that he was being made the object of an intolerable injustice goaded him on to disobedience, whatever the consequences may be.

"I'm waiting. Are you going to hand them over or not?"

The bullying voice of the policeman was angry and threatening.

"Neither of us gets them," Felipe said suddenly. And whirling them round his head, he threw the fins into the sea.

The policeman, shaking with rage, ordered him to come to the harbour Station. But Felipe, partly overcome with fury, partly out of pride, refused to allow himself to be arrested. Nobody could foretell the outcome of the scene. But, fortunately, an army officer who had come up, intervened. In an authoritative voice he ordered the policeman to control himself and told Felipe to allow himself to be taken to the station.

"You had better go. The policeman has to do his duty."

Felipe protested, gave reasons. The policeman was going to beat him.

"And I'm not going to take it. If he hits me . . ." and in his reticence there was an implicit threat.

Finally, he accepted a compromise. He would allow the lieutenant to arrest him, but not the policeman. The soldier, an exception to the rule, was a sensible man and agreed. The policeman also accepted the solution though unwillingly, because he considered his authority undermined. All the way to the station he was muttering threats.

And now, on his way to the sea-front, Felipe remembered it all. The policeman had not been satisfied, and would try to get his own back. He had got himself into a nasty business over those shark fins. When he reached the bar on the corner of Cuba and Carteles Streets, he saw the father of Congo, his fishing partner. He asked where Congo was and was told he had been on the beach for a long time.

He walked quickly. Suddenly, as he came round the old Maestranza de Artillería, his eyes were filled with the sight of a blue uniform, standing on the sea-front.

"I'm in for it now. It's that cop" he thought and for a moment felt like turning back. Any one of his friends would tell you that he was afraid of nothing, neither men on land nor foul weather at sea. No, he was not afraid, but why take risks? Still he was ashamed he had felt like running away. So he went forward resolutely, with a firm step, but with a nervous tension masking his basic anxiety.

He very soon discovered that his intuition had not deceived him. It was the same policeman, despotic and provocative like a fighting-cock. Congo had already got the boat against the wharf and was fixing the mast in readiness to unfurl the sail. As he came up, Felipe noticed the policeman was observing him.

"Foolishness," Congo was saying, continuing his conversation with the policeman.

"Foolishness?" said the policeman. "I'm boss around here. If that fellow gives any more trouble I'll beat his guts out."

Felipe, stinging under the crude threat, felt like hitting him, but he controlled himself.

"Look, man, lay off me. Wasn't yesterday's business enough for you?"

"Lay off you?" His voice was sarcastic, sharp like the point of a harpoon. "You'll soon find out what's what. The little lieutenant got you off last time, but you slip just once, and I'll beat the hell out of you."

Felipe still managed to keep himself under control. Speaking to Congo he complained: "Nice way to begin a day." The policeman jeered:

"Oh, you are all meek and mild now you've got nobody to defend you." There was such a concentration of sarcastic scorn in the voice that Felipe, beside himself with rage, jumped forward.

"To defend me against a thing like you ... you who ..."

The phrase stuck in his throat. His anger was choking him. A minute which seemed a century passed. He tried to speak but his fury was like a knot in his throat. Then, unable to articulate a word, it occurred to him that his silence might be mistaken for cowardice. This thought shook him like a blow on the jaw. The blood that was choking him spread from his throat to his eyes, from his eyes to his head. And then, blind and deaf with fury, he advanced towards the policeman, his fists raised.

The dry crack of a shot disturbed the morning quiet. Felipe without understanding how or why suddenly felt himself stopped. Then he slumped down on the water-front, his eyes gazing at the sky. Against the limpid blue, he saw a long, shining cloud. "Like mother of pearl," he thought. And he remembered with extra-ordinary clarity the delicate sea-shells which decorated his child-hood years. Some were perfectly white, others a more tender colour, a marvellous pale pink. He had lots of shells which he kept in boxes, mostly old shoe-boxes. "And now I must buy shoes for the kids because they are going around barefoot." This thought brought him back to reality. In a giddy succession of images he remembered his quarrel with the policeman. Did he actually hit him? An unspeakable lassitude, a sort of pleasant tiredness and feeling of comfort were relaxing his muscles. Suddenly he realized that he was dying. It was not lassitude or tiredness or comfort, it was his life leaving him. But he did not want to die, he could not die. It was his duty not to die. What would happen to his children? He must defend his life which was the life of his children, defend it with his hands, his feet, his teeth. His mouth was dumb as if it were already full of earth. But he was not dead yet. He tried to form a clear image of his children, but it kept slipping away, blurred and fleeting. In the distance, as if from miles away, he heard Congo's voice. Another voice. Other voices. He could not get the picture of his children clear. He could make out a vague, hazy outline as in a bad photograph. His heavy eyelids gradually closed. His mouth twisted in a desperate effort to speak. At last he was able to murmur: "My children . . . my . . . my . . ."

He trembled violently and then remained motionless and silent, still and mute, his eyes staring at the sky.

On his chest over the left breast, almost invisible, there was a small red hole, about the size of a five-cent piece.

(Translated from the Spanish by G. R. Coulthard.)

Nicolás Guillén

Born in Cuba in 1902, Nicolás Guillén is the most outstanding poet in a literary movement of the late 1920s which continued throughout the thirties and was given the name *Afro-Cubanism*. Like other writers connected with this trend, Guillén sought his inspiration in folk-songs, dances and music of the Cuban people, in which Spanish and African influences are blended. The poems are characterized by rhythmical nonsense words, many originally African, repetitions, by directness of appeal and at times a deliberate primitiveness. Many of his poems are, in fact, not only very close in manner and content to the popular songs of the Negro element of Cuba but also to songs sung throughout Spanish-speaking America.

SENSEMAYA: A CHANT FOR KILLING A SNAKE

Mayombe-bombe-mayombé!
Mayombe-bombe-mayombé!
Mayombe-bombe-mayombé!

The snake has eyes of glass;
the snake comes and coils itself round a pole;
with his eyes of glass, round a pole,
with his eyes of glass.
The snake walks without legs;
the snake hides in the grass;
walking he hides in the grass
walking without legs.

Mayombe-bombe-mayombé!
Mayombe-bombe-mayombé!
Mayombe-bombe-mayombé!

If you hit him with an axe he will die.
Hit him hard!

Do not hit him with your foot, he will bite,
do not hit him with your foot, he is going away!

Sensemayá, the snake.
Sensemayá,
Sensemayá, with his eyes,
Sensemayá.
Sensemayá, with his tongue,
Sensemayá.
Sensemayá, with his mouth,
Sensemayá——.

Dead snake cannot eat;
dead snake cannot hiss;
cannot walk
cannot run.
Dead snake cannot look;
dead snake cannot drink,
cannot breathe,
cannot bite.

Mayombe-bombe-mayombé!
Sensemayá, the snake—
Mayombe-bombe-mayombé!
Sensemayá, it is still—
Mayombe-bombe-mayombé!
Sensemayá, the snake—
Mayombe-bombe-mayombé!
Sensemayá, it is dead.

(Translated from the Spanish by G. R. Coulthard.)

Shadows that only I can see
my two grandfathers go with me.

Lance with head of bone,
drum of leather and of wood:
my black grandfather.

Ruff round his broad throat,
grey warrior's armour:
my white grandfather.

Naked foot, body of rock,
these from my black man;
pupils of Antarctic glass,
these from my white man.

Africa of dank forests
and heavy, muffled gongs—
I am dying
   (says my black grandfather)
Black water of crocodiles,
green morning of coco palms.
I am weary
   (says my white grandfather)
O sails of bitter wind
galleon burning gold.
I am dying
   (says my black grandfather)
O coasts of virgin throats
cheated with glass trinkets.
I am weary
   (says my white grandfather)

O pure sun of beaten gold,
caught in the hoop of the tropics
O pure moon so round and clear
over the sleep of monkeys.

How many ships! How many ships!
How many Negroes! How many Negroes!
What long refulgence of sugar-cane!
What lashes those of the slave-trader!
Blood? Blood! Tears? Tears!
Half-opened veins and eye-lids
and empty day-breaks
and sunsets on plantations
and a great voice, a strong voice
shattering the silence.
And O the ships, so many ships,
so many Negroes.

      Shadows that only I can see
      my two grandfathers go with me.

Don Federico shouts to me
and Taita Facundo is silent;
and both dream on through the night,
I bring them together.
                   Federico.
Facundo. They both embrace.
They both sigh. They both
raise their proud heads
under the high stars
both of the same stature
black anguish and white anguish
Both of the same stature.
And they shout. And dream. And weep. And sing.
And sing—and sing—and sing.

      (Translated from the Spanish by G. R. Coulthard.)

ELEGY

Over the sea came the pirate
messenger of the Devil,
with his steady fixed stare
and his monotonous wooden leg.

We must learn to remember
what the clouds cannot forget.

Over the seas,
with the hyacinth and the bull,
with flour and iron
came the Negro, to make
gold;
and to weep in his exile,
over the seas came the Negro.

How can we forget
what the clouds can still remember?

Over the seas,
the parchments of the law,
the rod for fraudulent measuring,
and the pox of the viceroys,
and death, to sleep
without waking,
over the seas.

A hard thing to remember
what the clouds cannot forget
over the seas.

(Translated from the Spanish by G. R. Coulthard.)

BALLAD OF THE RIVER SPRITES

Chase away the spirits
Chase away the river-sprites.

The muddy waters of the river
are deep and full of dead;
tortoise shells
black children's heads
At night the river puts out its arms
and tears at the silence
with its claws, which are claws
of a frenzied crocodile.
Under the screaming of the stars
under the incendiary moon
the river barks among the stones
and with invisible fingers
shakes the arches of the bridges
and strangles travellers.

Chase away the spirits
Chase away the water-sprites.

Dwarves with enormous navels
live in its restless waters
their short legs are bent,
erect, their long ears.

Help, they are eating my child,
his flesh black and pure,
they are drinking his blood
they are sucking his veins
they are closing his eyes
his big eyes like pearls.
Run, the bogey-man will kill you,
my pickny, my pickny
may your neck-string protect you.

Chase away the spirits
Chase away the water-sprites.

But Changó[1] willed it otherwise.
A hand came out of the water
and dragged him away—It was a water-sprite.
It opened his skull in two halves,
it put out his two big eyes,
it pulled out his white teeth
and made a knot with his legs
and made a knot with his arms.

My pickny, my little pickny,
My sorrow is dreaming
of the depths of your river
and of your little dry veins
and your little wet heart.

Chase away the spirits
Chase away the river-sprites.
Ah, my pickny, little pickny,
I told you it would happen.

(Translated from the Spanish by G. R. Coulthard.)

[1] The god of thunder among the Yoruba of Nigeria.

René Marqués

Born in Puerto Rico in 1919, René Marqués is perhaps the leading playwright and short-story writer of Puerto Rico. His writing is characterized by experiments in a variety of literary techniques. He is a Puerto Rican nationalist and much of his work is directly or indirectly anti-American.

DEATH

There is not only a being for death but
also a freedom for death.   Heidegger

The morning was warm and quiet, the insipid flavour of Sunday mornings. The cathedral bells could be heard clearly in the room at regular intervals. Yolanda had got up at eight o'clock and, as he had feared, was making as much noise as possible to wake him. But he had no intention of reacting to Yolanda's belligerence, and went on pretending to sleep. Finally, she snatched up her veil and went out, slamming the door hard. From the cathedral bells could be heard the last call to the nine o'clock mass.

He got up in a bad mood. His head was rather hot, but otherwise he felt well. Nevertheless, looking round him he felt the stifling smallness of the room pressing in on him. He felt he must go out, but he could not co-ordinate this feeling of urgency with the slowness of his movements. At last his body seemed to obey his will. He went into the kitchen and made a cup of coffee. He drank it in great gulps. He did not even notice he had forgotten to put sugar in it. His only thought was to get out as quickly as possible.

In the corridor he stopped, seized with indecision. He saw the steps before him and was afraid he might become dizzy. So he concentrated his attention on the contrasts of light and shadow. Each corner faded into a penumbra. The hand-rail, polished and bright, stood out clearly under the flood of light from the skylight. His eyes, travelling from the fifth to the ground floor, over the geometrical pattern of the stairs, with their sharp right-angles, made him feel slightly faint. Instinctively, he leaned on the hand-rail. After a brief hesitation he started to go down.

In the street, the sun struck at him mercilessly. A motor-cycle flashed by, brushing his trousers. Behind it came a truck loaded with policemen. Then another. And another. The tyres screamed loudly on the near-by corner. This unusual concentration of armed force and the exaggerated speed of the trucks was something alarming in the monotonous quiet of the old colonial town. But he did not bother to think about it.

He started to walk down the street. At first it seemed his mind was a blank. It was a pleasant feeling. It came almost as a surprise when his thoughts began to assume some form. Always the same form : life–death, death–life. On this particular morning he felt hypersensitive as on all mornings after drinking. He knew that in these conditions his thoughts would be clear and precise. So would his feeling of the certitude of death. Then something like a spiritual annihilation was breaking down his body.

When had it all started? Perhaps it was one day at the beach, watching the sea, the eternal rhythm of the waves : their inevitability, their destiny unchanged through thousands of years. Or perhaps it was another day when he had seen the ruins of the house where he was born. He tried to reconstruct the distant years, the appearance of the house with its balcony of whitewashed wood. But it was impossible. 'This' could not be 'that'. Or when he visited the Spanish fort and his hands had caressed the ancient stones and he had thought of the dead generations which had also touched those stones. He did not know when. But at some moment he had had a sharp awareness of time in relation to the immutable, and in relation to what changes by means of death. He had seen his mortality, acutely and painfully. And death had begun to lurk around his life, to torture his mind, to weigh on his thoughts.

Like an imperious need, the urgency of not thinking overwhelmed him. Perhaps it would have been better to provoke Yolanda's reproaches to have kept her with him. Yolanda never let him think.

Suddenly he realized with surprise that his wandering eyes were looking at a pair of woman's legs, in front of a shop window.

He was not sure whether they were bare or covered by glass stockings. But he did notice the red, slit shoes which were too small for the plump feet. The ankle, however, was slender, opening in a graceful curve towards the round full calves. A black silk skirt stopped his eyes at the knees. Yolanda's legs had a smooth slenderness which attracted him. Once he had told her they were beautiful stems for the lilies of her thighs. At first she was angry, but later she laughed aloud.

If only Yolanda would not behave like a wife. There were times in their life together when he felt married to her and this he hated. Especially when Yolanda decided she was going to make him into a useful man. Just now it sounded silly. But her decision had had the power of embittering their lives for several weeks.

Yolanda hated his alcoholic excesses. Sunday mornings were generally a session of morals and ethics. His Saturday night drinking bouts made her furious. It was at such moments when he wondered whether his union with Yolanda was not really a conventional marriage.

But Yolanda possessed a rare ability for rousing his desire. And he was grateful for the pleasure which came to his senses, without him having to use the tricks of the traditional hunt for the female. He would have preferred to have burned in his own fire rather than violate his indolence. Because action terrified him. Every calculated act meant *one step more towards death*.

Suddenly he noticed two men's feet behind the red shoes. Enormous feet, encased in black. There were stains of mud on the brilliance of the patent leather. Then the sharp crease in the trousers.

The little red shoes remained motionless, impassive in the dark, threatening presence of the male shoes. But the rounded calves gently assumed a sharp angle. His eyes followed the line of the legs to the waist. The hips, imprisoned in their black silk, had assumed, in adequate proportions, the curve of the calves.

The scene made him feel slightly giddy and he had to lean against a wall. But he felt an urge to observe the expression of the man and woman. He raised his eyes. A cry of terror strangled in his throat. He saw two cold, expressionless, petrified faces. Faces without blood, without muscles, sexless. Two livid masks looking without seeing at the display window. The horrible vision brought an awareness of death. He ran down the street with a feeling of madness.

In the confusion of his flight he saw the sign of a bar and was tempted to have a drink, but he was terrified at the thought of going into the strange place. He went by it and bumped into a passer-by. He scarcely heard his protests. He had been going to apologize, but the man's bald head reminded him of his employer. In his mind, the familiar, yellow, smooth, shining bald head gradually assumed monstrous proportions.

He forgot he was running from those livid faces. Indignation had suddenly blotted out the macabre vision. And he felt his body swept with hatred like a hot wave which rose from his feet.

Hatred of his boss was one of his most carefully cultivated sentiments. He almost felt a tenderness for this hatred. Yolanda was in the habit of declaring that his boss was an extraordinary being, the inevitable model, when she wanted to quote him an example of a practical man.

He had a vision of himself in the long narrow office on the first floor of the store. On the right of his desk, jalousies covered with dust opened on to the street. On the left a sort of low veranda which overlooked the ground floor of the shop. Because the first-floor office was nothing more than a spying-tower from which the deficiencies of the employees and the petty thefts of the customers could be observed. However, he sometimes thought of the first-floor veranda as the edge of a precipice, a dark, terrifying bottomless pit. The dry persistent sound of the cash-register reached his ears, tormenting him. It was perhaps one of the causes for the aversion he felt for his hum-drum work. Apart from his profound scorn for the customers. He did not like the boss's son either. That eternal, feminine, insinuating smile, which female customers liked so much, got on his nerves.

When he became aware of himself sitting in the office, he felt he had been cast there as a challenge to his abilities as a human being. He felt an urge to become part of that strange world. But then arose his fear of action. It was a relief in a way to think that the boss should always know what *he* should do. This was perhaps why the boss had no awareness of death.

The boss's self-assurance emphasized his own incapacity for

making a life. And he was aware of his impotence, the uncertainty of his destiny, his total ignorance of his relationship to the world around him. And the fear which clutched his heart. Fear because he was responsible for a life he could not understand. Every minute was a cross-roads beyond which lay the implacable necessity of action. Afterwards death. Always death. Fatal inevitable.

Yolanda had taken refuge in religion. It was a consolation. But this refuge was denied him. There is no refuge for a man who believes he has discovered he has not got a soul. Solitude. And always an obscure force urging him to act. He was crushed by this feeling of being urged on, endlessly, without any purpose.

The screeching of tyres on the road hardly shook him out of his state of distraction. Another truck-load of armed men. Without hearing the insults of the driver he crossed the street and entered a dark alley. The dampness of the alley made him shudder. He then realized he was soaked in sweat and thought of getting out into the sunlight. He went through the alley quickly and emerged into a narrow street of low buildings. He was surprised to see the large number of people in this unimportant street. Various groups blocked the way. In the middle of the street were groups of youths and young girls. The youths were wearing white trousers and black shirts, the girls a white uniform. They looked like trainee nurses. They were all pale and silent. He thought it must be a religious procession. But the atmosphere did not suggest the magnificence of Catholic processions.

Suddenly he understood when he saw the Puerto Rican flag. They were revolutionaries. They were going to march through the city. He felt tired and leaned against an electric-light pole so he could watch more comfortably. What did those madmen want? Apparently nothing. They were organizing themselves for a procession. They were unarmed and were not even encouraging each other with the usual shouts one hears at a political meeting.

The word 'politics' hovered for a moment in his mind like a lost comet. How he hated the sound of the word! He had never quite understood it, but on the few occasions when it came to his mind he related it with unintelligible rantings. Always the same gestures, always different voices, shouting out the same lies, always the same coloured rags put out by the same fanatical hands. And

now these people, for a change, wanted a revolution. He had a feeling of tremendous urgency when he looked at the weak, prema-
turely defeated bodies of the young revolutionaries.

But he was fascinated by the silence of the street, and he
thought he glimpsed *something* in their adolescent eyes which
stopped his laughter. It was a resolve, a will, an absolute self-
certainty. What did it mean? Was it just a superficial demonstra-
tion? Or was it a sign that somebody had discovered a way of giving
meaning to existence? Giving meaning to life *in spite of death*.

He felt a chill. But this time the sun was shining full on his
face. To make a decision. But again he stumbled against the thought
of death. He was flooded with anguish.

Until then he had thought of himself as alone in his anguish,
and although it was painful, there was comfort in the thought that
other people were not aware of being in life. That is why they lived
like automatons without experiencing the metaphysical fear that
tormented him. But now, all at once, as if dazzled, he began to
doubt. It was possible the others felt as he did and had managed to
solve the conflict. To make up one's mind. If only he could. If only
death were not in the way. Out of doubt was born hope. He felt
astonished, but with a new kind of astonishment. It was that
exalted, happy astonishment which precedes any revelation.

He noticed a stir in the multitude of spectators crowded along
the sidewalks. For a moment he could not discover its cause. But
then he saw at both ends of the street two groups of strange people.
They were police. In their hands he saw terrible modern weapons.
He thought of the adolescents. He looked at the centre of the street
and was surprised to see that they were going on with the organiza-
tion of the procession, coldly ignoring the presence of that threatening force. Could they possibly know that this was the cross-roads,
the terrible, implacable cross-roads which faced him every day?

The two groups of police spread out at each end of the street.
The onlookers were overwhelmed by a heavy silence. The preparation of the modern weapons could be heard like a series of whip-
lashes in the silent street. And he thought of life. Life which was
only a prelude to death. But this immediacy, this imminence of death.
What could the adolescents be thinking? Were they worried about
saving their souls or, like him, did they believe the soul does not exist?

The mutual indifference between the young revolutionaries and the uniformed men seemed absurd. It was as if the presence of one set was in no way connected with the presence of the other. And he wondered if it was not ridiculous to relate the black mouths of the modern weapons with the pale, anaemic faces of the youths. It was obvious that one group was going to kill and the other to die, but they seemed completely oblivious of each other.

Suddenly he saw the independence flag floating from a pole held up by a small, squalid-looking young man and at the same moment he heard the strident notes of the revolutionary hymn. The youths, organized in double file, were no more than about seventy in number. Pale and resolute, they started to march.

It was at this precise moment that the full force of his revelation struck him. To save your soul was a meaningless phrase. The important thing was to save your existence. And what is more, it is necessary to accept this possibility. Because by accepting it resistance was eliminated and freedom could be achieved. *Freedom to act*. To exist, to exist fully. He felt so stunned, he wanted to shout out his liberation. And he could not help experiencing a vague feeling of gratitude to the pale-faced revolutionaries.

He realized that the procession had started. They looked like children playing at soldiers. But he knew that in their solemn eyes they carried the weight of centuries. The police, on the other hand, appeared to see nothing special in the youths. They watched them approach, cold and indifferent.

Only a few steps separated the revolutionaries from the agents in blue uniforms and the bullets were a link between the two groups.

He saw how bodies began to break gently. He also saw how the onlookers, realizing what was happening, broke into a mad flight. He then observed that the black machines at the other end of the street were joining in the murderous fire.

The orgy of death seemed to be endless. And in the midst of the confusion he was surprised that he remained so lucid. He perceived the smallest details. His senses were monstrous antennae receiving waves. It seemed absurd, but something seemed to be missing among the thousand voices of that inferno. It was the sound of the band, which had been silenced. Only the boy with the cymbals, his legs shot away by the rain of bullets, slumped on the ground, was still beating his disks together. And the rhythmical sound of the metal, like a tragic accompaniment, produced an effect of madness. A charitable bullet stopped the beating of the cymbals. Farther off he saw a wounded youth struggling desperately to hold up the revolutionary flag.

It struck him that his revelation had come almost simultaneously with the death of the revolutionaries. The crowd had pushed him up against a wall and this had protected him from the bullets. But he felt free to choose. He watched the dying youth struggling to hold up the flag. And for the first time in his life he felt sure of himself. He pushed against the crowd that was crushing him. Desperately he opened a breach in the human wall. He stepped over fallen bodies. Blood from several wounded onlookers splashed on to him.

Panting, exalted, he reached the middle of the street. He jumped to the side of the dying revolutionary and the act of seizing the flag gave him a sensation of mystical elevation he had never experienced before.

The tattered flag floated on the breeze. The red stripes splashed the air with their blood-coloured tatters. Yolanda, the boss, the boss's son, the office were no longer part of this world. All his being was concentrated on the act of waving the revolutionary flag triumphantly, challenging the murderous bullets. Still, he realized that the flag, his country, the revolution had no meaning for him. What mattered was action. *It was the act of acting that was saving him.* His whole useless life had suddenly found a meaning which was expressed in the rhythmical movement of the flag over his head.

He felt a belt of fire round his stomach. It was not too painful, but his body doubled over as if a spring had broken inside him. He fell to his knees, concerned only with holding up the flag. A hot blast burned into his chest. The flag fell suddenly with his hand resting on the coloured rag. A thick sweetness began to invade his body rising from his feet. Before it reached his throat he was able to think "Can this be death?" But he had no time to make certain.

(Translated from the Spanish by G. R. Coulthard.)

Jacques Roumain

Jacques Roumain, who was a poet and novelist, was born in Haiti in 1906. His novels deal with Haitian peasant life, particularly with the voudou world in which most of the Haitian peasantry lives. The poem *Guinea* refers to the old belief among the slaves that when a slave died his soul returned to Africa, *Guinea* being the word used in Haitian creole for Africa. Roumain died in 1940.

GUINEA

It's the slow road to Guinea
Death will lead you there
Here are the boughs, the trees, the forest
Listen to the sound of the wind in its long hair
> *of eternal night.*

It's the slow road to Guinea
Where your fathers await you without impatience
On the road they talk
They wait
This is the hour when the streams rattle like
> *beads of stone.*

It's the slow road to Guinea
No bright welcome will be made for you
In the dark land of dark me:
Under a smoky sky pierced by the cry of birds
Around the eye of the pond
> *the eye-lashes of the trees open on decaying light*
There, there waits you beside the water a quiet village
And the hut of your fathers, and the hard ancestral stone
> *where your head will rest at last.*

(From *Anthology of Contemporary Latin-American Poetry*, edited by Dudley Fitts. Copyright 1942, 1947 by New Directions. Reprinted by permission of New Directions.)

Luis Palés Matos

Luis Palés Matos was born in Puerto Rico in 1915 and like the Cuban, Nicolás Guillén, he wrote Afro-Antillian poetry. His later work, however, is of a more personal and lyrical nature, whereas Guillén's writing became progressively more political in content. He died in 1956.

MULATA-ANTILLA

In you, now, mulatto girl of the Antilles,
I enfold myself in the warm Caribbean sea.
Slow sensual water of molasses
sugar port, hot bay,
with light at rest
gilding the clear waves,
and the sleepy bee-hive buzz
of people bustling on the shore.

And now in you, mulatto girl of the Antilles,
I sail the sea of my islands.
Electric ripples of hurricanes
stretch and curl in the curves of your body,
while over my ship falls, thoughtful and slow,
the night of your eyes.

Your empire-banana and coconut,
which aim their golden artillery
at the passing ship which leaves us
its smugglers' booty of blond tourists.
On the hurricane's pony, singing your song,
swarthy Valkyrie, with flashing spurs of lightning,
riding towards the green Valhalla of the isles.

Free and unbridled expanse, you are
love without restraint or haste;
in your womb my two races conjugate
their vital expansive forces.
Torrid love, love of the mulatto girl
rooster of rum, melted sugar,
aromatic gum which burns the marrow of the bone
with perfumes of sandalwood and myrrh.
With words of the Song of Solomon,
you are fair because the sun has looked on you.
Under your tongue there is milk and honey,
and ointments are poured out in your eyes.
Your neck is like the tower of David,
Pharaoh's mare, O Shulamite.

In you, now, mulatto girl of the Antilles——
Oh what a wonderful awakening in the Caribbean
wild colour which hits the high notes,
red hot music of joy
and burning goads of perfume
—lime, tobacco, pine—
buzzing their drunken voices
at the senses.

And in you, now, mulatto girl of the Antilles,
are the whole sea and land of my islands.
A symphony of fruits bursts forth
furiously in the perfume of your body.
Here in its green suit is the sour-sop
with its smooth delicate musseline
pants; here the star apple
with its childish milk; here the pine
with its soprano's crown—— All
all the fruits, oh, mulatto girl, you offer me
in the bright bay of your body
burnished by the tropic sun
Cuba, Santo Domingo, Puerto Rico,
fiery and sensual lands of mine.

And oh the burning rums of Jamaica
and oh the fierce calalou of Martinique.
And oh the night of Haiti, fermenting with drums,
impenetrable and voudouesque.
Dominica, Tortola, Guadeloupe,
on Columbus's sea, all hoisted,
on the Carib sea, all united,
dreaming and suffering and struggling
against pestilence, hurricanes and greed,
and dying a little every night
and again at dawn alive again,
because you, mulatto girl of the tropics,
are freedom singing in the Antilles.

(Translated from the Spanish by G. R. Coulthard.)

ACKNOWLEDGMENTS

The author and publisher are grateful to the following for their kind permission to include copyright material in this book:

George Campbell for the poems 'Holy be the White Head of a Negro' and 'Oh Solomon's Fair'; Errol Hill for the play 'Dance Bongo'; the Honourable Philip M. Sherlock and *Caribbean Quarterly* for the poems 'Pocomania' and 'Jamaican Fisherman'; John Hearne and David Higham Associates Ltd., London, for the short story 'The Wind in this Corner'; Michael G. Smith for the poem 'Jamaica'; Eric Roach for the poem *The Picture*; Ernest A. Carr for the short story 'Civil Strife'; Derek A. Walcott and Jonathan Cape Ltd., London, for the poems 'A Careful Passion', 'Ruins of a Great House' (from *In a Green Night*) and 'Travelogue'; Samuel Selvon for the short story 'Calypsonian'; Mervyn Morris for the poems 'The Day my Father Died', Birthday Honours' and 'To a West Indian Definer'; George Lamming and A. M. Heath and Co. Ltd., London, for the short story 'Birthday Weather'; Twayne Publishers Inc., New York, for the poems 'Flame-heart', 'North and South', 'The Lynching' and 'If we must die' by Claude McKay (from *Selected Poems of Claude McKay* published by Bookman Associates, New York); Enrique Serpa for the translation of the short story 'Shark Fins'; Nicolás Guillén for translations of the poems 'Sensemayá', 'Ballad of my two Grandfathers', 'Elegy' and 'Ballad of the River Sprites'; René Marqués for a translation of the short story 'Death'; New Directions, New York, for a translation of the poem 'Guinea' by Jacques Roumain (from *Anthology of Contemporary Latin-American Poetry* edited by Dudley Fitts); and Editorial Universitaria, University of Puerto Rico, for a translation of the poem 'Mulata-Antilla' by Luis Palés Matos.

Every effort has been made to trace the owners of the remaining copyright material, but without success. On hearing from the writers concerned, the author and publisher will be pleased to rectify the matter immediately.